Access and Equity

Promoting High-Quality Mathematics

in Grades 3–5

Edited by

Sandra Crespo
Michigan State University
East Lansing, Michigan

Sylvia Celedón-Pattichis
University of New Mexico
Albuquerque, New Mexico

Marta Civil
The University of Arizona
Tucson, Arizona

Series Editor
Marta Civil
The University of Arizona
Tucson, Arizona

NATIONAL COUNCIL OF
TEACHERS OF MATHEMATICS

Library of Congress Cataloging-in-Publication Data

Names: Crespo, Sandra, editor. | Celedón-Pattichis, Sylvia, editor. | Civil, Marta, editor.
Title: Access and equity : promoting high quality mathematics in grades 3-5 /
edited by Sandra Crespo (Michigan State University, East Lansing,
Michigan), Sylvia Celedon-Pattichis (University of New Mexico,
Albuquerque, New Mexico), Marta Civil (The University of Arizona, Tucson,
   Arizona).
Description: Reston, VA : The National Council of Teachers of Mathematics,
   Inc., [2017]
Identifiers: LCCN 2017046686 (print) | LCCN 2017052611 (ebook) |
   ISBN 9781680540123 | ISBN
Subjects: LCSH: Mathematics--Study and teaching (Elementary)--United States.
   | Multicultural education--United States. | Educational
   equalization--United States.
Classification: LCC QA13 (ebook) | LCC QA13 .A32924 2017 (print) | DDC
   372.7/049--dc23
LC record available at https://lccn.loc.gov/2017046686

The National Council of Teachers of Mathematics supports and advocates for the
highest-quality mathematics teaching and learning for each and every student.

Printed in the United States of America

CONTENTS

This book is part of a series that grew from a proposal by the Educational Materials Committee at the National Council of Teachers of Mathematics (NCTM) to develop a collection of books based on the Access and Equity Principle for school mathematics from *Principles to Actions: Ensuring Mathematical Success for All* (NCTM 2014). In embarking on this project, the editors of the different volumes and I looked at previous NCTM publications addressing equity—and at two series in particular: *Mathematics for Every Student: Responding to Diversity,* edited by Carol Malloy (2008–2009), and *Changing Faces of Mathematics*, edited by Walter Secada (1999–2002). We want to acknowledge these previous efforts, as these series have been an inspiration to our professional trajectories and to our thinking for this current set of books.

As this series, *Access and Equity: Promoting High-Quality Mathematics*, was being developed, a wider discussion on equity was taking place among several professional organizations in mathematics education. In his president's message of September 15, 2016, NCTM President Matt Larson writes, "The NCTM Board has officially reframed its equity work to focus on Access, Equity *and* Empowerment to capture the critical constructs of students' mathematical identities, sense of agency, and social justice" (Larson 2016, emphasis in original). Additionally, the joint position paper *Mathematics Education through the Lens of Social Justice: Acknowledgment, Actions, and Accountability*, by the National Council of Supervisors of Mathematics (NCSM) and TODOS: Mathematics for ALL (NCSM and TODOS 2016), served as a catalyst for this discussion. We hope this series presents a valuable, powerful, and timely contribution to these conversations.

The Access and Equity Principle states, "An excellent mathematics program requires that all students have access to a high-quality mathematics curriculum, effective teaching and learning, high expectations, and the support and resources needed to maximize their learning potential" (NCTM 2014, p. 5). All the books in this series offer strategies and tools to support teachers not only as they implement the Access and Equity Principle but also as they reflect on their students' empowerment. The series is a good companion for the joint position statement mentioned above (NCSM and TODOS 2016). The chapters in each book address a wide range of areas relevant to issues of access and equity in school mathematics, including beliefs about teaching and learning, curriculum aspects, and families and community knowledge as resources for mathematics instruction. They offer concrete examples to address several of the suggested actions listed in the NCSM and TODOS position statement.

This book and the others in this series address access and equity with a focus on diversity (e.g., culture, race, ethnicity, home language or languages, gender, economic status, disability) as an asset to teaching and learning mathematics. Within these diverse settings, the chapters provide examples of (but are not limited to) the following scenarios:

- Students collaboratively engaging in powerful mathematical discussions
- Teachers adapting instruction to meet the needs of all students while maintaining high expectations
- Assessment that takes into account the various ways that students demonstrate their mathematical thinking
- Curriculum that draws on the resources that all students bring to the classroom
- Teachers examining their own beliefs and expectations about teaching and learning
- Tools that encourage teachers to analyze and revise their lessons with an equity lens
- Teachers engaging in school and community partnerships

The four books in this series (pre-K–grade 2; grades 3–5; grades 6–8; grades 9–12) are aimed primarily at teachers, teacher leaders, and professional developers. The books are research based and practice focused; many of the chapters include classroom teachers as co-authors. In selecting the authors for the different chapters, the editors looked for a varied representation of areas of expertise to ensure a balanced series that covers different aspects of access and equity. A common perspective to all authors is a focus on diversity as a resource toward high-quality teaching and learning of mathematics. Such a perspective addresses the overall theme of access, equity, and empowerment through initiatives that are based on a deep respect for the communities with which we work. We learn with them and from them. The authors draw on ideas such as the importance of learning from students' and their families' out-of-school experiences and building on these funds of knowledge (González, Moll, and Amanti 2005) for mathematics teaching and learning (Civil 2007); students' use of home languages as a resource in their learning of mathematics (Celedón-Pattichis and

Turner 2012; Moschkovich 2013); Ladson-Billings's (1995) criteria for culturally relevant pedagogy in terms of academic success, cultural competence and critical consciousness (p. 160); the need to understand students' mathematical identity (Aguirre, Mayfield-Ingram, and Martin 2013); and an understanding of the sociopolitical nature of mathematics teaching and learning (Gutiérrez 2013; Gutstein 2006).

Specifically, the books in this series aim to support teachers in—

- expanding their thinking about access and equity in mathematics teaching and learning;
- understanding and addressing the obstacles to achieving access and equity;
- exploring productive and unproductive beliefs in relation to access and equity;
- examining the role of expectations in relation to access and equity;
- using mathematically rigorous and challenging tasks with a focus on access and equity;
- learning how to adapt mathematics curriculum materials so that they meet the Access and Equity Principle; and
- developing and sustaining school and community partnerships as fundamental to a commitment to access and equity.

Chapters throughout the series follow the same structure. They start with a practice-based vignette intended to introduce the main message or messages of the chapter. The authors then discuss how they approached the principle of Access and Equity, sharing specific resources and strategies they used so that readers can adapt them to their contexts. The final section of each chapter includes reflection questions or possible actions for readers to consider. This structure makes the books appropriate for individual reading as well as for book-club reading with a group of teachers or teacher leaders.

This series would have not been possible without the support and collaboration of many people. I want to thank the Educational Materials Committee at NCTM for giving me the opportunity to develop these books and trusting my judgment in my choice of volume editors and letting us decide how to structure the books. I am also very grateful to Joanne Hodges and Joe Wood for their guidance and patience answering my many questions on NCTM's guidelines for publication. Most of all, I want to thank the wonderful volume editors, who have worked tirelessly for months not only on the volumes that they led but also across the series to make sure that we have a coherent product. Their dedication, professionalism, and knowledge of the field are admirable. I have learned so much from working with them. Finally, the volume editors and I thank the authors who accepted our invitation to contribute. They gave us these rich chapters that underscore their commitment to developing teaching and learning environments grounded on a deep respect for the mathematical thinking of teachers, students, and their families.

Marta Civil, Series Editor

REFERENCES

Aguirre, Julia, Karen Mayfield-Ingram, and Danny Bernard Martin. *The Impact of Identity in K–8 Mathematics Learning and Teaching: Rethinking Equity-Based Practices.* Reston, Va.: National Council of Teachers of Mathematics, 2013.

Celedón-Pattichis, Sylvia, and Erin E. Turner. "'Explícame tu Respuesta': Supporting the Development of Mathematical Discourse in Emergent Bilingual Kindergarten Students." *Bilingual Research Journal* 35, no. 2 (2012): 197–216.

Civil, Marta. "Building on Community Knowledge: An Avenue to Equity in Mathematics Education." In *Improving Access to Mathematics: Diversity and Equity in the Classroom,* edited by Na'ilah Suad Nasir and Paul Cobb, pp. 105–17. New York: Teachers College Press, 2007.

González, Norma, Luis Moll, and Cathy Amanti. *Funds of Knowledge: Theorizing Practices in Households, Communities and Classrooms.* Mahwah, N.J.: Lawrence Erlbaum, 2005.

Gutiérrez, Rochelle. "The Sociopolitical Turn in Mathematics Education." *Journal for Research in Mathematics Education* 44, no. 1 (2013): 37–68.

Gutstein, Eric. *Reading and Writing the World with Mathematics: Toward a Pedagogy for Social Justice.* New York: Routledge, 2006.

Ladson-Billings, Gloria. "But That's Just Good Teaching! The Case for Culturally Relevant Pedagogy." *Theory into Practice* 34, no. 3 (1995): 159–65.

Larson, Matt. "A Renewed Focus on Access, Equity, and Empowerment." Blog post, September 15, 2016. http://www.nctm.org/News-and-Calendar/Messages-from-the-President/Archive/Matt-Larson/A-Renewed-Focus-on-Access,-Equity,-and-Empowerment/

Moschkovich, Judit. "Principles and Guidelines for Equitable Mathematics Teaching Practices and Materials for English Language Learners." *Journal of Urban Mathematics Education* 6, no. 1 (2013): 45–57.

National Council of Supervisors of Mathematics and TODOS: Mathematics for ALL (NCSM and TODOS). *Mathematics Education through the Lens of Social Justice: Acknowledgment, Actions, and Accountability.* Joint Position Paper. 2016.

National Council of Teachers of Mathematics (NCTM). *Principles to Actions: Ensuring Mathematics Success for All.* Reston, Va.: NCTM, 2014.

Introduction

Sandra Crespo, *Michigan State University*
Sylvia Celedón-Pattichis, *University of New Mexico*
Marta Civil, *The University of Arizona*

This book focuses on the challenges to access, equity, and empowerment that present themselves when students transition to the third through fifth grades of elementary school. Mathematics in these grades is often characterized by an overemphasis on computational skills, at times without meaningful contexts to support sense making, as well as a premature rush to mathematical abstraction. Mathematics education research has documented the long-term effects of such an approach to school mathematics for young learners (National Research Council [NRC] 2001). These studies show how elementary age students learn to give up their sense making in order to reproduce taught procedures and to focus on memorizing procedures that their teachers have shown them (Ball and Bass 2003; Wearne, Hiebert, and Campbell 1994).

For the past thirty years and through its various documents, the National Council of Teachers of Mathematics (NCTM 1989, 2000, 2014) has worked hard to counteract overemphasis on computational drills and algorithms by offering standards, professional development and teaching resources, and research-based recommendations to support more conceptual orientation to the teaching and learning of mathematics. Because school reform efforts are often sparsely adopted and more readily implemented in affluent schools (Goldstein 2014; Labaree 2010), the past twenty years have seen a widening opportunity gap between students attending well-funded schools and those attending under-resourced schools (Flores 2007). One important challenge is that elementary school teachers underestimate the mathematical potential of young students, especially of students from nondominant groups. This book explores challenges and strategies for attending to access and equity in reform efforts that seek to improve the quality of mathematics teaching and learning for all students.

The third through fifth grades are particularly important because it is during these years that educational inequalities begin to take hold in underresourced schools—urban as well as rural—that primarily serve minority students in high-poverty areas (Oakes 1990, 2005). Inequities in resources and learning opportunities account for much of the disparity in the educational attainment of students. Elementary school teachers in grade 3–5 classrooms face growing pressure to prepare students to take standardized assessments, which are used not only as a measure of students' learning outcomes but also as an indicator of the teacher's quality (Darling-Hammond 2010; Goldstein 2014).

One particularly underestimated challenge to educational equity is the students' experiences with the dominant language of instruction in the mathematics classroom. Because students in third grade shift from learning to read to reading to learn, attending to the linguistic demands that mathematics classrooms place on all students, in particular for emerging bilingual students, is critical to developing academic literacy. Emerging bilingual students who begin their education with home-language support for their learning in kindergarten through third grade are transitioned to English-only classrooms when dual language programs are not available in fourth grade onward (Baker 2011). Yet, dual language programs have been shown to be the most effective in educating emerging bilingual students (Thomas and Collier 2012). Thus, continuing the support of the students' home language in fourth through fifth grades and beyond is critical to making tasks accessible and mathematics classrooms more equitable (Aguirre et al. 2012; Khisty 1995; Moschkovich 1999; NCTM 2014; Turner and Celedón-Pattichis 2011).

In addition, students in third through fifth grades become acquainted with standardized state testing. The results of these high-stakes tests are often used by teachers and administrators to classify students into different ability groups (Cohen and Lotan 1997, 2014). These ability labels follow students, especially those who speak English as an additional language, into middle and high school (Valdés 2001). Unless parents, teachers, counselors, or administrators advocate for these students in order to change their educational trajectories, the labels remain and exclude students from enrolling in rigorous mathematics coursework (Celedón-Pattichis 2004; Celedón-Pattichis and Ramirez 2012).

Themes and Organization of This Book

The chapters included in this book address the aforementioned challenges through the following themes: reframing beliefs about nondominant students and communities (chapters 1, 2, 3, 4); addressing linguistic demands in mathematics classrooms (chapters 5, 6); attending to classroom participation structures (chapters 7, 8, 9), and providing professional development focused on culturally and linguistically responsive teaching (chapters 10, 11).

The first four chapters set the stage for the book by challenging deficit perspectives about students, especially nondominant students and communities. Chapters 1 and 2 focus on how our conceptions and beliefs about students and about mathematics orient teachers to designing school mathematics tasks and activities that are more or less responsive to students' funds of knowledge. Chapter 3 explores the mathematical thinking of special education students. It encourages us to see the potential in their nonstandard ways of thinking about mathematics and shows how to use clinical interviews to learn about the mathematical thinking of these students and to design responsive mathematics instruction. Chapter 4 focuses on students in high-poverty communities engaging with a yard-space design of their school and learning fourth-grade concepts such as area, perimeter, and fractions. This chapter encourages us not to underestimate the mathematical potential of students from marginalized communities and illustrates what culturally relevant mathematics teaching and learning can look like.

Drawing from an assets-based approach, the next two chapters address the linguistic demands that mathematics classrooms place on students, particularly emerging bilingual students. Chapter 5 describes how a teacher supports a third-grade student who is in the beginning stages of English language development and who has mastered all the mathematics of the elementary middle grades. Chapter 6 offers approaches for teachers to analyze the organization and the structure of word problems in English and in Spanish by going beyond vocabulary to focus on phrases that are available to emerging bilingual students to help them understand the content of what is being asked in word problems.

Sharing a theme of participation structures, the next three chapters center on approaches teachers can use to engage all students, particularly emerging bilinguals, in mathematics discourse communities. Through the exploration of multiplication concepts, chapter 7 highlights specific features of mathematical discussions that advance access and equity to mathematics for third-grade students. Chapter 8 focuses our attention on the need to establish mathematics classrooms where bilingual and multilingual learners excel through productive partnerships. Chapter 9 offers tools to create equitable participation in mathematics classrooms, to reflect on why some students overparticipate or underparticipate, and to encourage all students to listen to and learn from one another.

Finally, the last two chapters focus on professional development that can make an impact with culturally and linguistically diverse students. Chapter 10 discusses a university-district partnership to support teachers in creating mathematical discourse communities, particularly with English language learners. Chapter 11 describes a university-school district partnership to support teachers in culturally responsive mathematics teaching and to illustrate how this work can radically change the nature of assessment in a state.

Synopsis of Chapters

Chapter 1, "Confronting the Lies I Tell Myself," by Rebekah Berlin and Robert Q. Berry III, unpacks how Berlin examined her core beliefs about teaching and learning and how these beliefs can be used toward equitable mathematics instruction. Berlin's core beliefs are these: "Language matters,"—that is, the ways that school personnel discuss students matter if they are to adopt an antideficit approach to mathematics teaching; "Teaching rigorous mathematics is more than teaching content," which refers to the ways teachers use language, actions, and positioning to make content accessible to every student; and "All families are invested in the success of their child," which entails positioning students and families as resources and as integral to the long- and short-term mathematical success of students.

Chapter 2, "Learning to Think Differently: Rerouting the Whole Mathematics Trip," by Higinio Dominguez, explores equity in mathematics teaching and learning from the metaphoric view of rerouting the mathematical trips teachers take with their students. This approach entails encouraging students to think differently about the mathematics concepts that they are required to learn in these grades. The author explores a unit on addition in which a research team encouraged third-grade students from nondominant communities to think differently about the concept of addition, moving from an uncritical learning of the addition algorithm to a collective interrogation of the rigidity that characterizes algorithmic thinking. The chapter then discusses how thinking differently leads to powerful learning and can have implications for how we engage in discourse about access and equity in mathematics education.

Chapter 3, "Difference Not Deficit: Assessing Issues of Access in Mathematics for Students with Disabilities," by Katherine Lewis, argues that it is more productive to understand students with learning disabilities as having developmental or learning differences. To address the unique needs of these students, it is critical to intentionally assess the accessibility of the tools we use to teach and do mathematics. Lewis illustrates how one-on-one clinical interviews can be used to effectively assess students with learning disabilities. Lewis concludes by providing recommendations for adapting this approach for a range of disabilities and mathematical topics. Assessing and acknowledging these students' differences is a first step toward providing instruction that is truly accessible to all.

Chapter 4, "Balancing Acts: Design-Based Mathematics for Students Living with Trauma," by Maria del Rosario Zavala and Marianna Singwi-Ferrono, argues that equitable mathematics teaching demands creative connections within meaningful contexts, drawing on students' multiple strengths as artists, leaders, and critical thinkers. Over the course of a few weeks, fourth-grade students at a community charter school in East Oakland, California, worked in small teams to design a new play-yard space at their school. Students created a two-dimensional scale rendering of an irregularly shaped space. The teacher supported students to work collaboratively on key fourth-grade concepts such as area, perimeter, estimation of distances and areas, and fractions. The authors draw on evidence from the project to argue that creative design projects can be an important part of teaching mathematics to students with trauma in high-poverty urban schools when paired with pedagogies that set up students for success.

Chapter 5, "Moving the Mathematics Forward while Acquiring English," by Zandra de Araujo, Erin Smith, and Melanie Kremmel, focuses on an overlooked group of students, those who are mathematically above grade level and in early stages of English language development. The authors highlight Kremmel's experiences with Oksana, a third-grade student who moved to the United States from Ukraine. On arrival, Oksana's proficiency in English was in its beginning stages; however, her mathematical proficiency was far above a third-grade level. Within weeks Oksana had worked through all the elementary and middle grade level tasks that she had been assigned. Kremmel was then left to consider how to best support Oksana within her third-grade classroom. This teacher's experiences are not uncommon; however, much of the literature related to teaching mathematics with English learners focuses on supporting them linguistically rather than challenging them mathematically. The authors argue that teachers need interconnected strategies in both of these areas because students' mathematical learning cannot be put on hold while students acquire proficiency in English.

Chapter 6, "Bilingual Academic Development in Mathematics for Emergent to Advanced Bilingual Students," by Luciana C. de Oliveira, Sabrina Sembiante, and Andrés Ramirez, addresses academic language at the word, phrase or sentence, and discourse levels as an approach to access and equity in the mathematics classroom. This approach considers the organization and structure of mathematics word problems in both English and Spanish as a means of providing strategies for teachers to go beyond vocabulary and "key words" in working with emerging bilingual students. They provide examples of word problems in third grade to show how teachers can focus on language chunks to help students understand the content of what is being asked in the word problem and contrast language chunks in English and Spanish. This chapter shifts the dialogue from exclusive focus on language demands of academic texts for bilingual students to language affordances exclusively available to these students in dealing with language demands in the mathematics classroom.

Chapter 7, "Meaningful Mathematical Discussions That Matter," by Kathleen Jablon Stoehr and Puja Patel, opens with a vignette from a mathematical discussion in Patel's third-grade English Language Development (ELD) classroom, where students were discussing whether 4×3 was the same problem as 3×4. Using cats as the context in the problem, half of the students drew three four-legged cats while the other half of the class drew four three-legged cats. The vignette includes examples of how Patel facilitated her students' discussions of why they believed or did not believe that 3×4 was the same problem as 4×3 and how the class arrived at a final answer. The authors discuss specific features of mathematical discussions that advance equity and access to mathematics for all students, specifically for ELD students. These features include the potential of mathematical discussions that can enhance students' conceptual understanding of mathematics, shift the power structure of mathematics from teacher to students, create opportunities for all students to participate, and offer academic language support for ELD students.

Chapter 8, "Promoting Equity, Access, and Success through Productive Student Partnerships," by Kathryn B. Chval, Rachel J. Pinnow, Erin Smith, and Oscar Rojas Perez, illustrates how teachers in grades 3–5 establish mathematics classroom environments in which bilingual and multilingual learners flourish through productive partnerships. The authors use examples from classrooms and research to illustrate teaching practices that have facilitated equitable partnerships for bilingual and multilingual learners in mathematics classrooms. The authors introduce a framework that will assist teachers as they consider student characteristics for group work and establish classroom norms that promote perseverance in problem solving; engagement in beneficial mathematical discussions and arguments; and development of academic, communicative, and social competencies.

Chapter 9, "The Problem of Overparticipation: Fostering Productive Participation in Your Classroom," by Marcy B. Wood and Maggie Hackett, reframes achievement through the lens of participation. High-achieving students, because they frequently overparticipate, undermine the learning opportunities of their peers and of themselves. When low-achieving students underparticipate and the high-achieving students overparticipate, the class as a whole experiences unproductive mathematical discussions. This chapter offers tools for generating more equitable participation and for reflecting on why individual students overparticipate or underparticipate. It also describes ways of supporting overparticipators in becoming more aware of their participation patterns while simultaneously creating spaces and reasons for underparticipators to contribute their mathematical ideas and questions. Finally, the chapter emphasizes the considerable positive consequences of encouraging all students to listen to and care about the learning of others. By helping students and teachers focus on equitable participation rather than on achievement differences, teachers can improve mathematics learning for their whole class.

Chapter 10, "Professional Development to Support 'Integrated' Language and Mathematics Instruction for English Language Learners," by Rodrigo J. Gutiérrez and Galina (Halla) Jmourko, features a university–school district partnership. The authors describe a unique professional development experience aimed at improving mathematics instruction for English language learners. A school district English to Speakers of Other Languages (ESOL) coach and a university professor collaborated to offer seven focus group sessions for elementary classroom and ESOL teachers to develop their capacity for engaging ELL students in mathematical discourse. This chapter provides details on specific instructional tools and language supports that teachers adopted in their classrooms that resulted in a more nuanced understanding of the complexity of teaching mathematics with ELL students and increased repertoire of instructional strategies to address the needs of their diverse classrooms.

Chapter 11, "Stories from the Trenches: Urban Classrooms in Portland," by Emma Ford, Brian Greer, Michael Koopmann, Bijal Makadia, Swapna Mukhopadhyay, Mark Wilson, and Marsha Wolfe, features a university-school partnership that forms part of an initiative of the Oregon Department of Education to further its declared mission of producing a culturally responsive teaching force. The aim of this partnership project is to develop grade 3–5 teachers' ideas and ideals of culturally responsive mathematics teaching. The authors include activities that are in line with the philosophy of asset, as opposed to deficit, pedagogy (e.g., reaching out to the funds of knowledge within the children's homes and community; working toward a concept of culturally responsive assessment in mathematics). Teachers within the project report on positive interactions with their students and enhanced awareness of their identity as intellectual workers. The authors describe the deleterious effects on learning and teaching of excessive standardized testing, against the background of a move to radically change the nature of assessment in the state.

References

Aguirre, Julia M., Erin E. Turner, Tonya Gau Bartell, Corey Drake, Mary Q. Foote, and Amy Roth McDuffie. "Analyzing Effective Mathematics Lessons for English Language Learners: A Multiple Mathematical Lens Approach." In *Beyond Good Teaching: Advancing Mathematics Education for ELLs*, edited by Sylvia Celedón-Pattichis and Nora G. Ramirez, pp. 207–21. Reston, Va.: National Council of Teachers of Mathematics, 2012.

Baker, Colin. *Foundations of Bilingual Education and Bilingualism*. London: Multilingual Matters, 2011.

Ball, Deborah Lowenberg, and Hyman Bass. "Making Mathematics Reasonable in School." In *A Research Companion to "Principles and Standards for School Mathematics,"* edited by Jeremy Kilpatrick, W. Gary Martin, and Deborah Schifter, pp. 27–44. Reston, Va.: National Council of Teachers of Mathematics, 2003.

Celedón-Pattichis, Sylvia. "Rethinking Policies and Procedures for Placing English Language Learners in Mathematics." *NABE Journal of Research and Practice* 2, no. 1 (2004): 176–92.

Celedón-Pattichis, Sylvia, and Nora G. Ramirez. *Beyond Good Teaching: Advancing Mathematics Education for ELLs*. Reston, Va.: National Council of Teachers of Mathematics, 2012.

Cohen, Elizabeth G., and Rachel A. Lotan. *Working for Equity in Heterogeneous Classrooms*. New York: Teachers College Press, 1997.

————. *Designing Groupwork: Strategies for the Heterogeneous Classroom.* 3rd ed. New York: Teachers College Press, 2014.

Darling-Hammond, Linda. *The Flat World and Education: How America's Commitment to Equity Will Determine Our Future.* New York: Teachers College, 2010.

Flores, Alfinio. "Examining Disparities in Mathematics Education: Achievement Gap or Opportunity Gap?" *The High School Journal* 91, no. 1 (2007): 29–42.

Goldstein, Dana. *The Teacher Wars: A History of America's Most Embattled Profession.* New York: Anchor Books, 2014.

Khisty, L. "Making Inequality: Issues of Language and Meaning in Mathematics Teaching with Hispanic Students." In *New Directions for Equity in Mathematics Education*, edited by Walter G. Secada, Elizabeth Fennema, and Lisa B. Adajain, pp. 279–97. New York: Cambridge University Press, 1995.

Labaree, David. *Someone Has to Fail: The Zero Sum Game of Public Schooling.* Cambridge, Mass.: Harvard University Press, 2010.

Ladson-Billings, Gloria. "Toward a Theory of Culturally Relevant Pedagogy." *American Educational Research Journal* 32, no. 3 (1995): 465–91.

————. *The Dreamkeepers: Successful Teachers of African American Children.* San Francisco: John Wiley & Sons, 2009.

Moschkovich, Judit. "Supporting the Participation of English Language Learners in Mathematical Discussions." *For the Learning of Mathematics* 19, no. 1 (1999): 11–19.

National Council of Teachers of Mathematics (NCTM). *Curriculum and Evaluation Standards for School Mathematics.* Reston, Va.: NCTM, 1989.

————. *Principles and Standards for School Mathematics.* Reston, Va.: NCTM, 2000.

————. *Principles to Actions: Ensuring Mathematics Success for All.* Reston, Va.: NCTM, 2014.

National Research Council (NRC). *Adding It Up: Helping Children Learn Mathematics.* Washington, D.C.: National Academies Press, 2001.

Oakes, Jeannie. *Multiplying Inequalities: The Effects of Race, Social Class, and Tracking on Opportunities to Learn Mathematics and Science.* Santa Monica, Calif.: RAND Publication Series, 1990.

————. *Keeping Track: How Schools Structure Inequality.* 2nd ed. New Haven, Conn.: Yale University Press, 2005.

Thomas, Wayne P., and Virginia P. Collier. *Dual Language Education for a Transformed World.* Albuquerque, N.M.: Dual Language Education of New Mexico/Fuente Press, 2012.

Turner, Erin E., and Sylvia Celedón-Pattichis. "Mathematical Problem Solving among Latina/o Kindergartners: An Analysis of Opportunities to Learn." *Journal of Latinos and Education* 10, no. 2 (2011): 146–69.

Valdés, Guadalupe. *Learning and Not Learning English: Latino Students in American Schools.* New York: Teachers College Press, 2001.

Wearne, Diane, James Hiebert, and Patricia F. Campbell. "Place Value and Addition and Subtraction." *The Arithmetic Teacher* 41, no. 5 (1994): 272–74.

CHAPTER 1

Confronting the Lies I Tell Myself

Rebekah Berlin, *University of Virginia*
Robert Q. Berry III, *University of Virginia*

When I started teaching, I was a white middle-class woman teaching black children in a low-income black community, and I had very limited experiences and authentic relationships with black women, men, and children (an embarrassing fact to admit). This was also true of my authentic relationships with people who had grown up with fewer financial resources than my family had.

During a dismissal time in my first year of teaching, I let some of my female students touch and braid my hair. They told me how beautiful it was and that I should never cut it. When a parent pulled me aside and told me I needed to stop because I was reifying messages of whiteness, especially of white hair, as beauty, my response was, "I didn't even realize! I am so sorry!"

Contrast my response to a different situation my first year. During winter break, I began planning a fraction unit for my fourth graders, and a knot folded in my stomach when I realized I did not fully understand the meaning of fractions and their operations. I knew this was unacceptable. The knot was there because I was scared of the repercussions my ignorance would have on my students. Therefore, I read multiple books, applied for and attended professional development, and talked to colleagues to fill in my knowledge gaps so that my students would have access to high-quality instruction.

In the first scenario, someone else had to point out a way in which I was unprepared to serve my students. My reaction was to abdicate responsibility. This was based in an untruth: that I was actually the victim, a victim of ignorance and lack of exposure, rather than an irresponsible woman in a position of power over young children who are constantly messaged by media and people like me that their appearance is somehow less than mine. In the second scenario, I demonstrated a high sense of agency. I identified a gap in my readiness to teach my students, determined that filling this gap was within my control, and did so. Why did I treat these two events so differently?

Making a Commitment to Access and Equity

The two vignettes illustrate the complex relationship between beliefs about access and equity in mathematics. The second scenario demonstrated a productive belief found in *Principles to Actions: Ensuring Mathematical Success for All* (NCTM 2014). Berlin's certainty that her knowledge of mathematics would have an impact on her students' chances of success was rooted in the belief that her students' mathematical abilities were a "function of opportunity, experience, and effort—not of innate intelligence" and that mathematics teaching and learning "cultivate mathematics abilities" (NCTM 2014, p. 63). This productive belief positioned Berlin as a reflective teacher to examine whether her knowledge of mathematics content and pedagogy provided opportunities for her students to experience mathematics learning in meaningful ways.

In contrast, the first vignette demonstrated that holding only some (but not all) productive beliefs about access and equity is not enough for our students. The parent who informed Berlin of the implied messages and the potential impact of letting children play with her hair served as a community and cultural informant. This parent raised Berlin's awareness of how her whiteness can affect black children's worldview. Berlin's initial comfort with her lack of knowledge and experiences about her students' contextual and cultural backgrounds revealed an unproductive belief: "Mathematics learning is independent of students' culture, conditions, and language, and teachers do not need to consider any of these factors to be effective" (p. 63). Being knowledgeable about the culture conditions and contexts of communities provides opportunities for teachers to access sources of funds of knowledge to incorporate into their teaching. In this context, funds of knowledge is an approach to validate what families do outside school and to recognize them as intellectual and educational resources to support teaching and learning (Moll et al. 1992). Parents not only act as advocates for their children but also create opportunities for their children to learn mathematics in everyday, contextual realistic situations. Students bring into the mathematics classroom unique familial, cultural, and experiential backgrounds that serve as funds of knowledge. Teachers can seek out community resources (such as the parent in the vignette that begins this chapter) to support mathematics teaching and learning.

Positioning beliefs as productive and unproductive is a framework for unpacking actions and practices that affect access and equity. Beliefs for access and equity often are separated into two silos, one focusing on curriculum and instruction and one focusing on identity. These silos can provide different lenses for examining access and equity. Berlin stated, "In my early years of teaching I focused on achieving access and equity solely through curriculum and instruction, because it was more comfortable to debate the merits of pedagogical approaches to teaching fractions, or to analyze the quality of differentiation in my classroom, than it was to unpack my identity and assess its impact on my students." Unpacking one's identity in relation to the students and the community they serve requires teachers to seek and develop cultural and community knowledge and to develop critical and supportive allies. Both types of work, unpacking curriculum and instruction and unpacking identities, are necessary for access and equity in mathematics teaching and learning.

While the list of productive and unproductive beliefs in *Principles to Actions* (NCTM 2014) can help us interrogate our beliefs about students, it can also help us evaluate our beliefs about ourselves as educators. Such self-examination is crucial if we want our productive beliefs about students to affect their experience of mathematics. To make mathematics instruction accessible and equitable, we educators need to believe both that we are capable of making necessary changes and that it is our responsibility to do so. For example, to switch from the unproductive belief that students' experience of mathematics is divorced from their broader identities to the productive belief that "effective mathematics instruction leverages students' culture, conditions, and language to support and enhance mathematics learning" (NCTM 2014, p. 63), Berlin needed to believe that she could and should change her pedagogical practices. This chapter focuses on one strategy that Berlin used to maintain her sense of agency as an educator: the process of naming lies she accepted about her students or herself and the structures she put into place to resist these lies.

Advancing Access and Equity: Berlin's Voice

I lie, regularly. On rare occasions, I tell the lies you learn not to tell when you are little—the kind where you know something happened, but you tell a different story about it to other people, often to avoid some type of consequence. Far more often, however, I find myself engaging in a different and, I think, more dangerous type of lie. These are stories I whisper to myself in spaces of uncertainty as a method of self-preservation; I use them to avoid deeply uncomfortable truths about myself and other (almost always white) people I love or as a way to avoid doing work that I know will be very hard, work that I might not know how to complete successfully. These lies leak from my personal rationalizations to the narratives that I provide others about my experiences. In telling these lies to others, I build a community of allies that can uphold the image I want to paint of myself (most often an image of me as both savior and martyr). Therefore, instead of working toward equity as I espouse to, in these stories I maintain the status quo, which upholds white supremacy. In opposition to these lies are truths: I am the adult responsible for the experiences my students receive in my classroom, and it is my responsibility to make sure that these experiences promote access and equity.

In this chapter, I describe the lies that I find myself most frequently telling as a way to falsely limit my agency (and therefore responsibility). After each lie, I share a truth that stands in opposition to it as well as strategies that I use to change my behavior. This list is not exhaustive. It is designed to reflect the equal importance of content, pedagogy, and culture in the classroom. As you will see, it is also extremely reflective of my position as a white middle-class female educator who teaches black children.

Regardless of whether you find my lies similar to your own, the process of naming our lies is one that I recommend to all teachers for multiple reasons. First, by making ourselves name lies, we force ourselves to interrogate our actions and the narratives that we use to represent them. Second, by naming our lies, we are more likely to notice them in our behavior and in the behavior of others, often others that we love and respect. Third, in using the word *lie*, we force ourselves to acknowledge the willful deceit of ourselves and others as well as the harmful consequences of our behavior. Fourth, when we publicly name our lies, we can hold ourselves (and others) accountable. We can ask others to hold us accountable. The more we identify our own problematic behavior, the more we can work toward mitigating damage we have done and changing our future behavior.

> ***Lie 1:*** I'm so sorry. I didn't even know/think about . . . (Implied: How could I have known that?)
>
> ***Truth:*** I have the skills to learn about my students, their families, and their cultural backgrounds. It is my responsibility to acknowledge how much I don't know about those different from myself, and constantly work to fill in my knowledge and experience gaps.

This first lie often comes out of my mouth as a faux apology when I engage in an act of racial aggression toward my coworkers, my students, or their families. The vignettes at the beginning of this chapter demonstrate that despite the parallel problems I faced, I viewed my lack of knowledge and experience with cultures other than the one in which I grew up as different from my lack of knowledge of mathematics. Although I immediately sought ways to develop my knowledge of mathematics content and pedagogy, when faced with my lack of understanding of my students and their backgrounds, I believed that I was only a product of my experiences and that I could not be expected to be accountable for things that I did not know. A variety of factors contributed to my lack of knowledge, experience, and relationships, including the college I chose to attend, the classes I chose to enroll in there, the people I chose to be friends with at every level of schooling, the types of media I chose to consume, the places where I chose to hang out, and so on. What I want to make clear is that my ignorance was not by chance. It was the result of choices that I (and people I love and respect, such as my parents, but mostly I myself) made.

Strangely, this truth holds great hope. Once we acknowledge that our ignorance is of our own making, a series of choices rather than something that happened to us, we realize that there were alternative paths we could have taken and we can set a new course for the future. We can focus on gaining the knowledge and skills we need in order to move toward the productive belief that "effective mathematics instruction leverages students' culture, conditions, and language to support and enhance mathematics learning" (NCTM 2014, p. 63).

We can fill this gap in several ways. One is through reading. In my case, I chose books to help me learn new perspectives in the same way that I selected books to help me understand fractions. I have expanded my viewpoint about current and historical events by reading authors of color as well as authors who live in or are from communities similar to those of my students. Through reading, I find tremendous gaps in my knowledge of history as well as immense bias in the history that I thought I knew. Reading has also helped open my eyes to things I did not know to look at, such as the historic connotations of the differences in skin color and hair texture between my students and the way these influenced dynamics in our classroom.

Another way to address this gap is to learn, from multiple perspectives, the history of the community in which you work. When I did this, I discovered a history of white faces like mine systematically robbing the neighborhood where I worked of its resources. They shut down the factories that provided jobs, abandoned these factories so they became designated hazardous waste sites, left the housing market when black families moved in, cut the neighborhood off from the rest of the city with an interstate highway (it was bounded on the other sides by river and swamps), largely ignored schools that were woefully underpreparing children because their children did not attend them, made the choice to pull out grocery stores because they were not as profitable as they were in other sections of the city, and ruled to put major waste repository sites adjacent to the school I worked in. Learning this history, as well as the broader history I spoke of in the preceding paragraph, helped me begin to unpack what my identity as a white woman might mean to my students and their families. I began to develop (and continue to do so) eyes to see the way my whiteness affects every single aspect of my life, though it was most noticeable to my untrained eye at my job. My whiteness signaled that I was not only an outsider but also a member of the powerful elite who, to protect their position in the social hierarchy, consistently abused and ignored women, men, and children in our city and in our nation who looked like my students and their families. My whiteness meant that if something ever went wrong in my classroom, my version of the story is the one that would have been told and protected. This is not to say that I now know everything about either the history and culture of the students and families I worked with or my own white skin. It is to say that my evolving understanding of the weight of my identity led to a new level of intentionality about my interactions with students and their families.

The history of the community in which you work and the effect that aspects of your identity have on your students and their families might look very different from what I have described. However, if we do not make this type of work a habit, we almost surely will not develop socially, emotionally, and academically safe spaces for mathematics teaching and learning.

> **Lie 2:** It's not an ideal outcome but I did the best I could, given the circumstances . . .
>
> **Truth:** All students can and want to learn. If students are not developing socially, emotionally, or cognitively, I am responsible for figuring out why that is and making it happen.

I use this lie when I do not want to accept responsibility for my students' outcomes. I try to avoid this responsibility for a couple of reasons. First, it is uncomfortable; it means that I have to acknowledge my shortcomings in the classroom. Second, it means that I am going to have to do a lot of work, first to learn about ways to improve my practice, and second to actually implement the improvements. Below I discuss four areas I examine when I am trying to pinpoint the ways in which I am and am not providing the "differentiated supports (e.g., time, instruction, curricular materials, programs) necessary to ensure that all students are mathematically successful" (NCTM 2014, p. 63). They are not groundbreaking or glamorous suggestions, but I list them because, although many of us would like to think our classroom is a safe, exciting, caring, and efficient place, there is often room for improvement.

The first method I suggest to combat the lie of "I did my best" is to record your lessons and watch them. I have found that regularly recording myself and watching the videos is extremely helpful in identifying room for improvement. When I look at videos for issues related to classroom management, I see obvious signals, such as behavior that is so disruptive that it prevents students from learning; but subtle parts of management erode the quality of learning in our classrooms, too. On video it was easy to see when I overlooked students who were not disruptive but were not engaged, either. It was also easy to see when a lack of quality routines and procedures resulted in wasted instructional time. Video allowed me to examine the frequency, length, tone, and content of my interactions, helping me see if the story I told myself of what happened during my mathematics block matched what I saw on the video.

Second, examine who is doing the cognitive work in your room and at what level they are working. Student work was one of the most helpful ways I held myself accountable to the productive belief that "all students are capable of making sense of and persevering in solving challenging mathematics problems and should be expected to do so" (NCTM 2014, p. 64). In my early years in the classroom, I prided myself on the differentiated small-group instruction that I enacted. But each day, when I examined student work, I had to confront the fact that only certain groups succeeded with their work and ask myself what I had done to cause that outcome. I began to notice that I had a tendency to give some students work that was not appropriate to their readiness level (e.g., multiplication word problems that required the same visual and written explanation as those given to their peers, but that had smaller numbers to allow these students to use concrete objects to model the action first) but was instead flat-out easier (e.g., rather than having to provide a representation or justify their answer, they just had to write the answer to naked number problems). Again, I found videoing my classroom to be a useful practice. In watching myself on video, I noticed that I accepted different levels of depth in written and oral responses from different students. Video revealed that, with some groups, I ensured that students were doing almost all the cognitive work. It also revealed, however, that I would sometimes feed answers to struggling students to save time or so they could feel success.

Another system that I found helpful for interrogating the equitability of my interactions with students was to keep a two-pocket folder for mathematics conferences in my classroom. In the left pocket were sheets of paper, each with a student's name on it and a space where I could take notes. Whenever I observed or conferenced with a student, I moved that student's sheet from the left pocket to the right pocket. Once I had moved all the sheets to the right, I began the cycle again. What was shocking to me was how frequently I wanted to grab for sheets that I had already moved to the right (signaling I had recently conferenced with that student) and how many students I might have overlooked without the accountability system as a reminder. In short, left unchecked, I had several tendencies that would have exacerbated inequity in my room.

Third, ask yourself about the extent to which you actually scaffold high expectations. It is one thing to say, "I want my children to have rich mathematical discussions in peer groups," another thing to plan for it, and yet another thing to execute what sometimes feels like trivial steps toward the final outcome. If I wanted to see any particular behavior in my classroom, I carefully broke down, executed an incremental rollout, and checked for mastery of subskills before asking students for the full behavior. For example, when I wanted my students to critique the mathematical arguments of others, I first had them practice agreeing, disagreeing, and citing evidence to support their claims with general, not mathematical statements (e.g., The sky is pink). This exercise focused my students' cognitive efforts on the complex discussion skills I wanted them to build, rather than splitting their efforts between new discussion skills and new mathematical ideas. Only when my students proved that they were fluent with pinpointing precisely what they agreed or disagreed with, and could support their critique with evidence, did we begin to apply these skills to engage with new mathematical content.

Most often when I noticed students were not engaging in something the way I hoped, I had rushed some stage of the process above. Some of the behaviors I planned to foster among students included the following: resolving conflicts with other students; using self-regulation strategies when frustrated; documenting and sharing solution strategies; accessing and using tools in the classroom (e.g., manipulatives, anchor charts, supplies); working in groups with other students; and transitioning between different classroom areas. They are not the only behaviors I planned to address in my classroom, but I highlight social, behavioral, and cognitive outcomes in the list above to underscore that these all factor into successful mathematics instruction and that we educators have the ability to influence each of them.

This process of carefully breaking down and planning for productive engagement also applies to teaching and learning mathematics content. For a host of systemic reasons (some that I mentioned earlier in this chapter), my students often came to me behind grade level. According to pretests, most of my third graders entered with a late kindergarten to early first grade proficiency with mathematics. This was largely an exposure problem, and it meant there was a great deal of content that they needed filled in.

I worked in a district with a strict pacing guide, common assessments, and a mandated scripted curriculum. I had a coach who observed me, met with me to debrief my observations and lesson plans, and planned monthly meetings for all the teachers in my grade level across the district, during which we analyzed data from common assessments. The district resources were aligned to a pacing guide for an on-grade-level third grader. These resources would have wasted valuable time when every second with my students needed to be focused on covering the most essential elements of three years' worth of instruction—in one year. Although a part of me wanted to say, "I was told to do this so I have to do the best with what I have been given," in reality this was not true. Following the district pacing guide and using the district lesson plans, while significantly more convenient, would not be in the best interest of my students.

There were many ways I could have chosen to take responsibility for the mathematics my students learned that year. Ultimately, I decided to carefully break down, prioritize, and remap the content I covered based on the foundational skills my students needed to master third-grade content, the content of future grades, and the mathematics they would encounter in daily life. I planned my own long-term plan, unit plans, and daily lessons, and created my own assessments. I had difficult conversations with administrators at my school and district about why I was not following the district's guides and plans. I list my processes here, not so that they may be replicated, but to show that there are often more factors that contribute to our students' mathematical success within our influence than we would like to acknowledge. To reiterate the truth of "I am responsible," we are not victims of our students' content readiness. If students are not succeeding in mathematics, we need to examine their foundation, find the gaps, and fill them in.

> **Lie 3:** We can only expect so much, given their home situation . . .
>
> **Truth:** All families are invested in the success of their child. It is your responsibility to build a partnership with families and guardians in service of student success.

Authentic relationships take time and effort. Unsurprisingly then, my colleagues and I consoled ourselves with the above lie when we wanted an immediate or easy fix to a problem we were having with a student. I sometimes felt myself buy into this lie as early as the first day of school. Every year when parents would meet me for the first time, I would watch their faces fall. Some of them would say things like, "You? You're my child's teacher?" in a voice that suggested what they were really asking was, "What did we do to deserve this?" During my first few years in the classroom, this reaction offended me. I wanted to shoot back a copy of my résumé so these parents could see my track record with students at our school, the student achievement data, and video footage that showed I had performed in the top percentage of my district each year I taught. Embedded in my anger was the idea that somehow, because someone had allowed me to claim a position of power over their child, I deserved instant loyalty, trust, and, if I was really being honest with myself, compliance with my vision for the year.

This is a dangerous, colonialist mindset. Parents did not owe me anything. They did not have to trust me; they did not have to like me. I was in a tremendous position of power, often with their child for more hours in the day than they were. This was a gift. My students' parents had every right to feel alarmed when they saw me, including for reasons I outlined under the first lie. Further, the city's education system had been failing the community I worked in for so long, and many parents I worked with entered the year with negative associations with schools and teachers. Additionally, the way I taught mathematics was very different from the way most of the parents I worked with had learned it. Given all of this, what is surprising is not that parents were openly nervous that I was their child's teacher; it was that I somehow hoped they would not be.

To counter this mindset, I had to acknowledge that parents were going to need a substantial amount of evidence, sustained over a long period, before they began to feel that I was worthy of being with their child each day. Again, authentic relationships take time and effort. Part of how I attempted to establish trust was through transparency. I wanted parents to feel that they knew what was going on in my classroom at all times. I invited parents to sit with their child in our classroom to see our approach to mathematics. I also called and texted parents regularly. I provided updates on their child's progress in the classroom, snapshots of their child's work, and occasional pictures and video of their child.

This volume of communication proved beneficial in many respects. Building relationships across lines of difference is difficult but especially so when a student is struggling. Because I had frequent contact with parents, communication was less jarring if I needed to express concerns about a student's behavior or growth in our classroom. My concerns could be expressed on an established platform of my knowledge of and belief in their child. As time went on, I found that parents would call or text me about problems they saw at home and ask me for advice, and we would come up with ways I could support the student at school. We were able to become partners enveloping the entirety of the student's day.

In the community in which I worked, parents commonly switched phone numbers or sometimes had no phone. When I first started teaching, I took this as a free pass, one less call to make, one less text to send. I quickly realized, however, that I was losing my most important teammates in supporting my students when I allowed something like a lack of cell service to block our communication. I combated this obstacle in two main ways. First, my students lived in close-knit communities. Everyone was somebody's cousin, biologically or fictive; and many of the families shared child care, groceries, and transportation. To contact someone, typically all I needed to do was ask the student or one of the student's friends for an aunt's or uncle's phone number. I could then ask the aunt or uncle to provide me with the parent's new number or to put me on the telephone with the parent. More commonly, I just walked home with my students, because during my last two years of teaching I was lucky enough to work for a district with dismissal procedures that included walking students home. Although the obstacles you face to communicate effectively with parents and the methods you use to overcome those challenges might look different from the ones that I discuss here, what is similar across teaching contexts is that relationships with parents are not something we are owed, nor we should expect them. Rather, they are something we need to cultivate consciously and creatively in service of student success.

Notably, the more I went to my students' homes, the more the people in the community knew me, and the more I was given access to community information that I could use to support my students. I want to be clear I was not posing as a spy, trying to see what was going on in the homes of my students. What I hope to emphasize is that when we conceptualize our work as a commitment to our students' opportunities and growth, rather than as a place we go to from a certain time in the morning until a certain time in the evening, we expand our influence and become available for authentic and powerful partnerships.

Reflecting and Taking Action

The Access and Equity Principle in *Principles to Actions* states that "all students [should] have access to a high-quality mathematics curriculum, effective teaching and learning, high expectations, and the support and resources needed to maximize their learning potential" (NCTM 2014, p. 59). In this chapter, Berlin showed us how she uses her lies to examine issues of access and equity by unpacking her beliefs and practices in her classroom to empower students to engage in mathematics in productively meaningful ways (see also chapters 7 and 9). In Berlin's truths and lies, we see overlaps with the actions proposed for teachers in the Access and Equity Principle in *Principles to Actions* (NCTM 2014, p. 115).

After you have read this chapter, we hope that you are able to reflect on the lies that you may tell yourself. As you reflect, consider these questions:

- Reflect on Berlin's lies and truths. What are your truths and lies regarding the teaching of mathematics?

- What are the narratives and actions that surround your truths and lies? That is, how do your lies play out in your school, community, and context?

- What are the consequences of your truths and lies regarding students' learning of mathematics?

- How can you build accountability structures to push back on your lies and to move forward your truths?

References

Moll, Luis C., Cathy Amanti, Deborah Neff, and Norma Gonzalez. "Funds of Knowledge for Teaching: Using a Qualitative Approach to Connect Homes and Classrooms." *Theory into Practice* 31, no. 2 (1992): 132–41.

National Council of Teachers of Mathematics (NCTM). *Principles to Actions: Ensuring Mathematical Success for All.* Reston, Va.: NCTM, 2014.

CHAPTER 2

Learning to Think Differently
Rerouting the Whole Mathematics Trip

Higinio Dominguez, *Michigan State University*

> *Imani*: Because, when you do it, uh, in the equation [*points to 428 + 335 written in horizontal format*], you usually start with that [*points to the 1s position*] in case, uh, it's more than 10, because if you start with the 100s, you go four hundred, seven hundred [*adds the 100s*]. Then twenty, fifty [*adds the 10s*]. Then 8 plus 5, it's 13 [*adds the 1s*], and then it's harder, but, it's not really hard.
>
> *Higinio*: It's not that hard, right?
>
> *London*: Yeah, that is for me.
>
> *Imani*: You COULD start with the 100s if you wanted to.

Making a Commitment to Access and Equity

The above conversation occurred toward the end of a unit on addition and subtraction co-designed and co-implemented by a teacher and a mathematics education researcher. The school is in a working-class neighborhood in the Midwest and serves a large population of students from nondominant communities. Racial, cultural, linguistic, and socioeconomic differences exist both among students and between students and teachers. In 2013, the teacher of the students in the vignette welcomed the opportunity to take part in a participatory research project focused on promoting reciprocity between teachers and students in diverse mathematics classrooms. When teachers must follow scripted curricula that envision teaching as telling and learning as following instructions, reciprocity disappears and with it the possibility to see difference as a resource rather than as a threat to knowledge construction. Like the other teachers in the project, this teacher learned to make space for reciprocity in her mathematics instruction. Her commitment to access and equity centers on promoting reciprocity with and among students. The mathematics instruction that this teacher and the other teachers enact resembles collective inquiries with a level of complexity that requires a variety of ideas and perspectives. As these multiple ways of knowing and understanding emerge, they help teachers come closer to their students' lives, experiences, and diverse epistemologies.

The unit from which the vignette is drawn is an example of these collective inquiries. The teacher embarked with her students on the collective study of how best to organize addition both from a practical, authentic point of view and from a more formal mathematical perspective. The collective units of study that this teacher (and others) prepared are complex educational interventions (Bell 2004) that ignite teachers' curiosity regarding how new knowledge can emerge. During co-planning sessions, it is common to hear teachers say, "I can't wait to see how my students will take that idea." These teachers are curious to see how new knowledge intersects with students' diverse epistemologies, cultures, and languages. These units of study constitute collective opportunities to learn to think differently about a mathematical concept and about those who are learning the concept, including teachers, students, and their researcher-collaborator. The teacher in this classroom wanted to design a unit that would support her students in approaching the standard algorithm for addition and subtraction with a more flexible and critical understanding. She had noticed that her students chose the standard algorithm as their preferred method even when they could not explain how the algorithm worked. The standard algorithm has been challenged in research for its limitations in supporting students to solve problematic word problems (Contreras and Martinez-Cruz 2007).

Advancing Access and Equity

The reciprocity that teachers have been able to restore as part of their work transforming their teaching practice has allowed them, as well as the researcher-collaborator, to develop a more complex view of access and equity than that described in *Principles to Actions: Ensuring Mathematical Success for All* (NCTM 2014). Although the Access and Equity Principle highlights the importance of creating opportunities *for students* to learn important mathematical concepts, our vision of embarking in collective inquiries *with students* implies that these opportunities are also *for* teachers and mathematics education researchers. Central to how we understand opportunities to learn is our view that learning is not restricted to students. In our collective units of study, students, teachers, and the researcher-collaborator learn in connected ways. Research has not recognized this collective learning, particularly its connectivity.

The co-planning of collective inquiries challenges the unidirectional notion of providing *access* for students to mathematical knowledge. Although the language of access may be easier to understand (or may seem to have more impact), it also suggests a "knower-known" situation, in which the knower (student) either has access or is denied access to knowledge. We do not support this language. The teachers in the reciprocity project do not merely provide access to opportunities to learn, as suggested by the language in *Principles to Actions*. Because the collective inquiries are collaborative, the issue of access shifts its focus from students to both teachers and students and moves toward a system in search of more meaningful teaching and learning. As the teacher, students, and researcher-collaborator take new directions in their learning, new knowledge emerges for all. These new directions allow them to think differently about mathematical concepts. When people think differently about something, that is learning, as described in the following mathematical trip that the teacher and the researcher-collaborator co-designed.

Planning a New Mathematical Trip

During the planning of a collective inquiry on how to promote addition strategies that made sense to a group of third-grade students, the teacher mentioned to the researcher-collaborator that the school principal was driving to Flint, Michigan, every weekend to deliver bottled water to people affected by the water contamination crisis there. From this conversation, a powerful image began to emerge of students organizing the collection of bottles of water in an efficient way in order to create inventories. We asked ourselves, "How would the students add to and subtract from these organized inventories?" We had envisioned a new direction for our co-teaching, and this new direction was fertile with possibilities for the emergence of new knowledge.

First, we thought how students could both learn mathematics and use that learning to address a social justice issue. As the teacher said, "My students care about what is happening right now in Flint. Some of them even have relatives who live there!" Second, the water crisis offered opportunities for students to make their own groups of bottled water, naming and renaming those groups, and to justify the effectiveness of those groups for adding and subtracting bottles. We assume that the process of making—e.g., making their own groups, making packaging boxes—would co-emerge with richer, more flexible ways of understanding addition (Roth 2016). Third, the conceptual development of addition and subtraction, as envisioned in this teacher-researcher conversation, had the students with one foot in the mathematical ideas and the other in actions that supported not only the mathematical ideas but also the goals of addressing a pressing issue in their community. In a search for related readings, we found an article that grounded the concept of addition and subtraction in the concrete action of packing and unpacking (Whitenack et al. 2001). This reading became our road map to the new route we wanted to take with our students.

A Collective Inquiry Leading to Collective Learning

We began the unit by asking the students what they knew about the water problem in Flint. They said: "Their water was polluted and they don't have any fresh water"; "The pipes are dirty"; "The factories are poisoning the water a little bit"; "It poisons people"; "It poisons plants"; "It poisons the animals that's in the water"; and "They can't drink water, they only can drink water out of bottles."

I posed a question: "How many bottles of water do you think the people in Flint would need?" Numbers suggested ranged from the tens to the millions, with the thousands being the most popular suggestion. I then personalized these suggestions by showing them their teacher's bottle of water and asking them, "How many bottles of water like this do you think you can drink in one day?" The numbers offered this time gravitated toward the three and five, with some students trying to impress with numbers still in the tens.

The teacher then told the students that the school principal was delivering water to institutions in Flint where people are young, old, or ill. She said that, during the previous weekend, they had filled two rental trucks with bottled water to take to Flint. The teacher then proposed to her class, "I have an idea. What if we bring bottles of water as our donation to the people in Flint?" One student, curious about one detail, asked, "But where do we put them?" I revoiced the student's question for the whole group to hear. They responded, "Here, in the classroom." I asked, "Why is it important to know where to put them?" The students answered with a number of ideas. The first one had to do with efficiency, not having to move the water out of somebody's way. Another idea had to do with accumulation and the need for a larger space to store the water. Yet another idea had to do with not losing any bottles. After acknowledging all these ideas, I offered a scenario: "Let's say that I am the principal and you have been bringing bottles of water during the whole week. At the end of the week, I come into your classroom to get the water. What do I need to know?" Students said, "You need to know where they are"; "You need to know where are they and like, how much is, how much are they, how much bottles of water are they." Hearing students agree with the importance of knowing how many bottles of water we had, I asked, "Why do I need to know how many bottles of water?" Students replied: "Because it's for different people"; "So that you can fit them in your car"; and "You can decide if you have enough to bring, and if you don't know, you may not bring enough, and people might have to wait while the other people have water, so if you don't have enough, you may decide to wait until this day." Students' readiness to role-play with me, as suggested by their enlivened responses to my question, suggested their ability to address a critical situation while focusing on the important aspect of organizing quantity. When we heard these responses, the teacher and I exchanged smiles because we both knew that we had rerouted our mathematics trip in the right direction. We also knew that the opportunity to learn included us.

In the following days, the teacher and I asked the students to suggest the optimal size of a package so when someone came into their classroom, he or she would almost immediately know how much water they had collected so far. Fives, twenties, and tens soon filled the air, until students converged to the idea that ten was the "easiest way to package water." The teacher and I wanted the students to run into the need to develop a larger package when these packages of ten eventually became too many to count. Neither of us suggested the next package size, because we trusted that somehow the need for a larger package combined with the students' prior knowledge would cause this new knowledge to emerge. In fact, one student commented, "When we first started counting the bottles, we didn't have the 100s first, we had the 10s. When we started making the 100s is when Elias had more room in his box of 10 to put more in there. So that gave us the idea of how to name these 100s [points to 100s box], so that's how it was really easy for us to do it."

As we engaged the students in the physical organization of groups of tens, hundreds, and single bottles, the teacher and I created pictorial representations on the board. We suspected that the standard algorithm that had been taught to these students left no room for the multiple and continuous translations between the embodied cognition involved in physically, intellectually, and discursively organizing water and the more symbolic, disembodied representations of that activity. We, in other words, wanted the students to experience mathematical meanings as both palpable and thinkable phenomena (Radford 2009).

Thinking Differently about Addition

As our collective inquiry unfolded, the teacher and I noticed a group of four African American girls who represented quite well the transformations achieved in students' ideas regarding the standard algorithm. We therefore decided to interview (see chapter 3) this group at the end of the unit, to have a representation of perspectives both consolidated and condensed for future analysis. In the interview, I sat on the carpet with the four girls, Imani, London, Naila, and Melody. I placed two sheets of paper in the middle of the circle we formed and asked them how many bottles of water we had (see fig. 2.1).

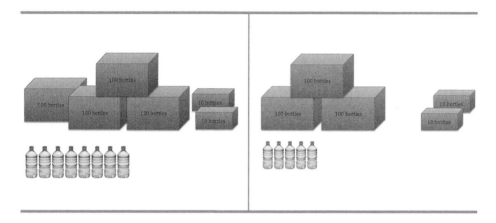

Fig. 2.1. Water bottle problem

The four students approached the problem in different ways. Naila first regrouped the eight and five bottles into one extra package of ten and three single bottles. Then she focused on counting the hundreds, then the tens, and then the ones. Melody declared that while she was counting the ones first, she was simultaneously listening to the other girls counting the hundreds and tens; so by the time she had finished adding the ones, she already knew the other sums of hundreds and tens. Imani preferred to add the hundreds first, then the tens, and finally the ones, which resulted in an extra ten that she added to her sum of tens. In contrast, London's explanation suggested that she struggled in following the approach her peers had used. When I wrote the numbers represented on each sheet into the horizontal format equation $335 + 428 = ?$, all the girls but London immediately recognized the equation as representing the drawings on the sheets: "Wait, is that the same as what we just did?" London, instead, immediately rewrote the equation in vertical format and executed the standard algorithm. So then I asked them to talk to me and to one another about whether they had added from hundreds to ones or the other way around.

Melody:	I just, I usually go the smallest ones, 'cause it's a lot easier for me, and for me it goes a lot faster.
Imani:	Um, I'm going to have to disagree with her way, for me. I also can see how it works for you, but not for me, because if I were given this I would have to know the number, so I'm going to count like this, so 1, 2, 3, 4, 5, 6, 7, 8; 9, 10, 11, 12, 13, and then I would go by the 10s, 10, 20, 30, 40, 50, 50 plus 13 is, 63, and then, uh, I would have to add the 100s, 100, 200, 300, 400, 500, 600, 700; and then I would have to add 63 to 700, which would be easy, that would be fast, but the whole thing isn't very fast because if I had something that I could time myself it would, the way, that I count like this, 4, 3, 700 [*pointing to 100s*]; 2, 3, 50; 8, 5, 13; 63, 763; that's easier. I wish we could time ourselves, but we can't.
Higinio:	I think I just saw it and you went faster. What do you think, Melody?
Melody:	Well, in my opinion, I'm used to going from smallest to largest [*Higinio:* You're used to] because I'm growing, that's how I'm being raised that way, my, my, my mother and father don't really go for math lately, but uh, one of, my friends, they are teach..., they're coming to our house and teaching me math, and, and they're teaching me how to do it just by 1, 2, 3, so I'm getting used to it.
Higinio:	So you're not used to counting 100s first, and then 10s, and 1s, you're used to the other way around, right?
Melody:	Uh-hum.
Higinio:	So are you [*Imani*] also used to counting the smallest ones and then the largest ones?
Imani:	No, I never really did the smallest to largest, because I think these are easier, because you can go like 100, 200, like that, and then the 10s you do that too, and when you do the ones, and it's on here, it takes longer to count, because you have to go, 1, 2, 3 . . .

While Imani was explaining her approach, Melody was inspecting the numbers in the equation. In the meantime, London and Naila were observing and listening. Then Melody explained:

Melody:	Yeah, because uh, I just noticed that, because, uh, I just noticed something. Because these two numbers [*4 and 3 in the hundreds place*] are a lot easier, then so, I just noticed this, so, when I do problems like this, and the two beginning numbers are easier, I

would start with those first, so that I, so then I would know the answer, so then I could just add them up.

Encouraged by what students were noticing—the new ways of thinking about addition that emerged along the road—I returned to London to see if she was also generating new knowledge.

Higinio: So let's ask London, how would you put these two together?

London: So, basically it was way harder this way [*using the horizontal format equation*] so I do it, usually my way [*points to vertical algorithm and walks me through steps*].

Higinio: That's the way you're used to.

Imani: I'm used to that way too [*referring to the vertical algorithm*], but sometimes, you can do it this way [*the horizontal format*] if it's, kind of easier, like this, I mean, I didn't have to add anything, cause I already knew the answer.

I changed the original numbers to 647 + 335 and asked them for their ideas, no writing yet, about how they would put these two numbers together. Following their noticing that "easy digits" in the hundreds place would make the problem a candidate for adding the hundreds first, I kept the problem similar to the original. I also wanted to see if discussion around a similar example would make London see what the other students were seeing. Leila, Imani, and Melody had helped me and one another see flexible ways of thinking about adding three-digit numbers. Now it was our collective turn to help our friend London see what we were seeing. So Imani drew squares and explained that this way the others could see it. She drew 6 boxes and 3 boxes for the hundreds, then 4 sticks and 3 sticks for the tens, and then little squares for the ones.

Higinio: So, London, what do you think these are?

London: 6 hundred.

Higinio: And the 3?

London: 3 hundred.

Higinio: And what is 6 hundred and 3 hundred?

London: 9 hundred.

Higinio: And then?

[*London adds the 4 and the 3, and says that's 70.*]

Higinio: And then? And then you add 5 + 7. And what is that?

London: 12.

Higinio:	So what do you do with that 12, 'cause you have 900, 70, and then 12, so what do we do with that 12?
London:	I can't do it like this [*horizontal*].
Higinio:	'Cause it's hard?
London:	For me it is!
Higinio:	Well . . .
London:	I like it my way. [*We all laugh.*]
Higinio:	But see, you have some work done! And I feel like you, know, you're kind of like throwing all that away. You have 970 figured out already. Imagine, 970 is already figured out, all you have to do is, you have 12 more, right? So what is 970 and then 12 more?
London:	Nine hundred and eighty-two.
Higinio:	All right, sister! That's a new way, right? It's not your way, but it's a new way, right?
London:	Yeah.
Higinio:	Now, isn't it good to have more ways than just one way?
Melody:	It's good to have more ways because if everybody had the same thing, it won't be interesting 'cause you already know, you already know what it is, and people have other, other, uh . . . ideas, then it'll get a little more interesting because some, some of them are faster, and some of them can slow down, they're all of them interesting.

Imani then explained to all of us how she would choose a method depending on whether she thinks the problem is easier or harder (e.g., to solve easier problems, she goes for the hundreds first; harder, she goes for the ones first). She wrote the algorithm to explain what she would do in case of a hard problem.

Higinio:	So London, you do it this way [*using Imani's algorithm*] because you think it's hard.
London:	That is hard.
Higinio:	Here's one thought. Things are easy when we're used to them, right?
London:	Yeaaaaaaah.
Higinio:	So maybe this way is not that hard; it's just that you're not used to it, right?
London:	No, I'm not.

Learning to Think Differently: Some Successes and Challenges

As participants in this collective inquiry, we experienced both successes and challenges. We discuss the successes first; then we look at some challenges and how we continue to think about them.

The greatest success for the teacher and researcher-collaborator was to see many students thinking differently about addition (see chapter 7 for multiplication problems). In the interview, they provided us with evidence of how they were abandoning mechanical approaches to addition and instead were noticing the kinds of digits the numbers included to guide their decision of whether to add from left to right or the other way around. Another success we noted was how seeing addition in a different way positioned students to argue in favor of different methods of addition and to use these arguments to convince peers of the value of thinking differently about these mathematical concepts. A third success was related to how we, the teacher and the researcher-participant, were able to learn from what is possible. In the case of this collective inquiry, we learned about the importance of connecting making with thinking (Roth 2016). We also learned that in order to design a unit of study in which students experience mathematical meanings both as palpable and thinkable phenomena (Radford 2009), the unit must be grounded in an important issue that is close to the students' experiences, and it must make room for students to guide the collective inquiry.

A number of challenges emerged for us. Perhaps the most important as mathematics educators was that not all students showed that they had changed the way they were thinking about addition. The teacher's interest in seeing this change developed from noticing that her students equated addition with the algorithm, often resulting in mistakes that students were not able to recognize. The researcher's interest echoed the teacher's, believing that student-generated methods would allow students to better understand the concept of addition. Yet, this change was more difficult for some students (such as London) than for others. We believe that changing the way one thinks about something is difficult in general. More collective inquiries of the kind we co-designed might allow us to see more students changing their mathematical thinking. Another challenge is how to choose issues, problems, and situations that allow students to change the way they think about a mathematical concept. There is, of course, no one single way to address this challenge. In our experience working with multicultural groups, the social issues that affect the communities where these students live seem to be fertile ground for engaging the students' diverse ideas about those issues and for molding those ideas into mathematical solutions. To address this challenge, we must rethink what matters in students' lives and ask ourselves, "Are our students interested in sharing candy, cookies, and toys; or are they more interested in sharing possible solutions to issues that affect their social and mathematical lives?"

Reflecting and Taking Action

Before these students, their teacher, and the researcher-collaborator rerouted this mathematical trip, most students—including Leila, Imani, Melody, and London—were seeing addition of multidigit numbers as something to be done primarily through the standard algorithm. Diverse ways of learning had been compromised in this case by previous instruction that favored one way of seeing addition. As co-designers of this rerouting, the teacher and the researcher-collaborator had an anticipated sense—rarely discussed in educational research—that by taking our students on a different path to knowing addition, issues of equitable mathematics teaching and learning would become evident. The new path—conceived initially as a way to stimulate students intellectually—encouraged students, the teacher, and the researcher-collaborator to engage in discussions, decision making, idea revisions, and conjecture making, all in ways that none of us had seen before in our mathematical teaching and learning together. The relational engagement and emotional investment seen among all learners—us included—suggested that inequity in mathematics instruction is inequity for both students and teachers. Put differently, our effort at correcting something that we had initially perceived as inequitable for our students—their adherence to one way of understanding addition—turned out to be an effort at correcting a situation that was inequitable for the teacher as well. The joy the teacher reported as a result of seeing with her students new ways of thinking about addition suggested that face of inequity that looks at teachers rather silently.

We found inspiration in the principal's trips to Flint. He was doing something most principals or most people may not do. He was attending to a real community need in an actionable way. Similar to the principal's actions, the teacher wanted to do something different about her teaching of addition and subtraction. Initially, she did not know exactly what to do or how. The researcher-collaborator also felt the kind of uncertainty that accompanies the construction of new knowledge. What was clear to both of us was our commitment to support her students to become more critical users of the standard algorithm.

Soon after we began implementing the water unit, the teacher and I realized that it made sense to think about an issue of access to clean water. However, we struggled to apply this metaphor of access to the issue of thinking differently about addition. Our struggle had to do with the fact that, although clean water exists—in this case, away from people who need it—the process of learning to think differently does not exist independently from the learner. Each day during the unit implementation, something new emerged: a new arrangement of ten bottles; a redesign of a box to hold the bottles; flexible ways of adding hundreds, tens, and ones; students' justifications for these new ways of adding numbers. None of these ideas pre-existed in the same way that fresh water does, which made us re-examine our "access" metaphor. In fact, the newer ways of approaching addition that students were sharing with one another reminded us that we, as co-designers of this rerouted trip, had much to learn from the students' ideas. We concluded that narrow instruction narrows intellectual growth for all, including the teachers. How much does our thinking about addition grow when our approach to teaching addition privileges only one way of thinking?

Based on our collective experience in this addition unit, a more generative metaphor for how teachers can teach diverse students is to think of mathematics units of study as collective inquiries. These inquiries should emanate from a shared curiosity regarding how an intellectual detour can promote new ways of thinking. There was excitement in anticipating what students would do along the rerouted trip. There was collective learning, which we defined as thinking differently, and this collective learning included us: the teacher and the researcher-collaborator. Most importantly, there was a sense at the end of the unit that this was not the end of the trip but only the beginning. Instead of thinking about giving students such as London "access" to new ways of thinking about mathematics, we prefer to think that the issue of equitable mathematics teaching requires a more complex view and, hence, a different language to describe it. We hope that in this complex view we will find the possibility of interrogating the discourse of access in order to think differently about that which we desire to change, feeling comfortable and embracing the uncertainty inherent in change (Stinson and Bullock 2012). In our unit, both knowers and knowledge continuously changed in ways that neither the teacher nor the researcher-collaborator anticipated, thereby making notions of access as concerned with students as with teachers. Our experience in rerouting this mathematical trip encourages us to pose the following questions for reflection:

- When we teach mathematics in one way, what other ways are we not considering and why?

* What opportunities exist in our local contexts to inspire us to teach and learn mathematics differently? (See chapters 4 and 11.)

* What would embracing a view of equity that includes us teachers make us do for our students and for ourselves?

- What can we do to enter our classrooms each day with a plan for making mathematics learning dynamic, evolving, and never the same as the day before?

Acknowledgments

This chapter is based on research supported by the National Science Foundation (NSF) under Grant No. 1253822. Any opinions, findings, conclusions, or recommendations included in this chapter are those of the author and do not necessarily reflect the view of the NSF.

References

Bell, Philip. "On the Theoretical Breadth of the Design-Based Research in Education." *Educational Psychologist* 39, no. 4 (2004): 243–53.

Contreras, José N., and Armando M. Martinez-Cruz. "Solving Problematic Addition and Subtraction Word Problems." *Teaching Children Mathematics* 13, no. 9 (2007): 498–503.

National Council of Teachers of Mathematics (NCTM). *Principles to Actions: Ensuring Mathematical Success for All.* Reston, Va.: NCTM, 2014.

Radford, Luis. "Why Do Gestures Matter? Sensuous Cognition and the Palpability of Mathematical Meanings." *Educational Studies in Mathematics* 70, no. 2 (2009): 111–26.

Roth, Wolff-Michael. "Growing-Making Mathematics: A Dynamic Perspective on People, Materials, and Movement in Classrooms." *Educational Studies in Mathematics* 93, no. 1 (2016): 87–103.

Stinson, David W., and Erika C. Bullock. "Critical Postmodern Theory in Mathematics Education Research: A Praxis of Uncertainty." *Educational Studies in Mathematics* 80, no. 1–2 (2012): 41–55.

Whitenack, Joy W., Nancy Knipping, Sue Novinger, and Gail Underwood. "Second Graders Circumvent Addition and Subtraction Difficulties." *Teaching Children Mathematics* 8, no. 4 (2001): 228–33.

CHAPTER 3

Difference, Not Deficit

Assessing Issues of Access in Mathematics for Students with Disabilities

Katherine Lewis, *University of Washington*

For the past five years, Ms. Fuentes, a white, middle-class woman, has been teaching fifth grade at Seaside Elementary, a racially, linguistically, and socioeconomically diverse school. She is deeply committed to providing rich and meaningful instruction to her students but is particularly passionate about mathematics. When she was deciding between several potential teaching positions, a big factor was Seaside's commitment to equity and inclusion. All students with disabilities were included in the general education classes, with special education teachers and paraprofessionals providing assistance for students when needed.

Since her first year at Seaside, Ms. Fuentes has been implementing problem-based learning to engage the diverse learners in her classroom. Each year she has worked hard to develop classroom norms around group participation and to engage her students in learning meaningful and conceptually rich mathematics. At the start of this year, she reviewed the Individualized Education Programs (IEPs) for students who would be in her class. Samuel was identified as having an emotional behavioral disability, Carla and Fernando were identified as having specific learning disabilities in reading, and Ryan was identified as having a specific learning disability in mathematics. Now, two months into the year, she was pleased with how Samuel, Carla, and Fernando were doing in mathematics, but she was seriously concerned about Ryan's progress.

Ryan was an attentive student, always did all his work, and received help from his parents at home, but was still struggling. Ms. Fuentes noticed that Ryan generally took longer than most students to solve problems, but he was not off task. He often counted on his fingers when solving basic arithmetic or multiplication problems and sometimes made errors when solving subtraction or division problems. Ryan often appeared to understand a concept initially but would have difficulty when trying to use that same concept a week later. During a recent unit of study, for example, the students had worked on finding the surface area of various shapes. Although in the first week Ryan seemed to understand how to calculate the area of rectangles, he was not able to calculate the area of a rectangle the following week when it was part of finding the surface area of a prism.

During a planning meeting, Ms. Fuentes brought up her concerns with Ms. Mitchell, the special education teacher. Ms. Mitchell said that Ryan might benefit from being pulled out during mathematics time for more direct instruction. She explained that students with mathematics disabilities often cannot understand the concepts and have to be shown step-by-step how to do the problems. She suggested that the problem-based learning approach used in class might not be structured enough for Ryan to understand the mathematics. Ms. Fuentes felt strongly that focusing solely on the step-by-step procedures and physically separating Ryan from the rest of his peers was in direct conflict with her goal of equity. But she knew she had to do something. Ryan was struggling, and the instruction that was working for her other students was not working for him. Ms. Fuentes was left wondering how she could change her instruction to meet Ryan's needs.

Making a Commitment to Access and Equity

Principles to Actions: Ensuring Mathematical Success for All (NCTM 2014) identifies the need for more equitable mathematics instruction for all students, including students with disabilities. Although students with disabilities are not often explicitly addressed within the access strand, I argue that disability is an important dimension of diversity that teachers need to address to create equitable classrooms. Just as race, language fluency, and socioeconomic status are often problematically framed as deficits, there is a tendency to understand disabilities as deficits as well.

Viewing students with disabilities through a deficit lens happens so routinely that it seems like common sense to do so. Assessments are used to identify holes or gaps in a student's mathematical knowledge, IEPs often specifically quantify a student's deficits, and teachers who are unsure of how to design instruction to address these students' needs often call on special educators to provide remedial instruction. Many times, this instruction is focused on addressing the gaps in the student's knowledge and removes the student from participation in regular mathematics instruction (Van Garderen et al. 2009). The rigor of the mathematical work frequently is changed: It becomes focused more on procedures, with the goal of helping the student practice a specific lower-level skill or complete a specific task, rather than develop an integrated understanding of the mathematical concepts (Karp 2013; Van Garderen et al. 2009). These traditional practices of separating students with disabilities from their peers and providing different instruction in a segregated place is directly in conflict with the Access strand in *Principles to Actions* (NCTM 2014). Dedicated and well-meaning educators— like Ms. Mitchell in the preceding vignette—often unconsciously take a deficit perspective for students with disabilities. Although it is tempting to see the "problem" as being within the student and to attribute the student's difficulties to a disability, this perspective has problematic ramifications for equity. When we believe that a student's struggles are caused by an inherent characteristic of the student, we are less likely to see instruction as a means to address the student's difficulties, thereby limiting a student's opportunities to learn (Jackson, Gibbons, and Dunlap 2017; Wilhelm, Munter, and Jackson 2017).

Instead of thinking of disabilities as deficits, it is more productive to understand these students as having developmental or learning *differences*. Students with disabilities have a biological difference (physical, perceptual, or cognitive) that leads them to develop in qualitatively different ways (Vygotsky 1993). These differences are part of natural human variation and therefore should be understood as an aspect of student diversity. I use the phrase "students with different abilities" rather than "students with disabilities" to highlight this focus on difference rather than deficit. These differences can have real consequences for the students' access to the mathematics instruction. The same high-quality mathematics instruction may not be equally accessible to all students. For example, a blind student might have issues accessing the visual components of a lesson; a student who is Deaf might be unable to access the spoken components of a lesson; and a student like Ryan, with a difference in how he neurologically processes number, may have difficulty accessing the representations of quantities used in the lesson. Therefore, access for students with different abilities is not just about providing high-quality mathematics instruction. We also need to consider the *accessibility* of the mathematics instruction itself. By focusing on access, we shift our gaze from identifying the "problem" within the student to identifying the issues of access in the instruction or mathematics itself.

Ms. Fuentes had determined that her instructional approach was not working for Ryan. The next step was to figure out why. To address the unique needs of students like Ryan, it is critical to intentionally assess the accessibility of the tools we use to teach and do mathematics. In this chapter, I illustrate how a one-on-one clinical interview can be used to effectively assess students with different abilities. Clinical interviews with students can provide insight into the student's prior knowledge and enable a teacher to evaluate what kinds of instructional approaches or tools might be more or less accessible. To describe this approach, I provide an overview of the features of clinical interviews and then present examples of a clinical interview focused on fractions and conducted with a student who, like Ryan, has a different ability in mathematics. Clinical interviews can directly inform the design of differentiated instruction, which provides students with alternative ways to access the same rich mathematics content (Lynch, Hunt, and Lewis, in press). I conclude by providing general guidelines for educators who are interested in using clinical interviews with their students.

Advancing Access and Equity

A clinical interview (Ginsburg 1997) is a one-on-one assessment technique that is particularly appropriate for use with students who struggle, whether or not they have an identified disability. Unlike standard written assessments, which provide little information about *how* a student understands the mathematics or *why* a student is struggling, the primary goal of a clinical interview is to understand a student's thinking. In a clinical interview, the interviewer (e.g., the teacher) poses a series of open-ended questions to the student. The student is asked to make his or her thinking visible by using words, drawings, or manipulatives. Unlike more formal assessments, the clinical interview is deliberately nonstandardized (Ginsburg 1997).

Although a set of predetermined questions is helpful to guide and structure the clinical interview, the teacher has the flexibility to ask probing questions and to explore potential hypotheses about the student's understanding. One unique aspect of this assessment is that it inverts the traditional roles of teacher and student. The teacher is the learner, attempting to make sense of the student's thinking; and the student is seen as the expert, because only the student can explain how he or she is making sense of the mathematics. Not only does the clinical interview provide valuable insight into the student's thinking, knowledge, and difficulties, but it also is ideal for working with students who struggle, particularly students with different abilities. A clinical interview can be a useful tool to identify a student's current understanding and to assess the student's access to various mathematical tools. By asking a student to represent, interpret, and use standard representations of quantities, the interviewer can determine if the student understands these tools in nonstandard and potentially problematic ways. An atypical understanding of representations suggests that these tools may be less accessible.

To illustrate how a clinical interview can be used to identify potential issues of access, I present excerpts taken from clinical interviews conducted with a student ("Emily") who was identified as having a learning disability specific to mathematics (Lewis 2014). Emily was a white, upper-middle-class, native English speaker who, like Ryan, was in a classroom that used problem-based learning approaches in mathematics and in a school with an explicit commitment to equity. Emily had been struggling with fractions, and these clinical interviews focused on assessing how she represented and interpreted fractions. Several of her answers revealed that she understood these representations and manipulatives in atypical ways, which may have made area models less accessible for her. These examples serve to illustrate common elements of a clinical interview and to provide an example of an issue of access, in this case with area models. In the first example, I asked Emily how she would represent the fraction 1/2. See figure 3.1 and table 3.1 on the following page.

Fig. 3.1. Emily's written answer to the question "How would you draw or write one-half?

In this first example, I asked an open-ended question, encouraged Emily to make her thinking visible, and asked her to explain each of her answers. In this brief exchange, I gained insight into Emily's current understanding of fractions. Emily provided two different ways of representing the fraction 1/2. Her answers and elaborations provide evidence that she knows not only how to represent one-half in fractional form (1/2) but also that it is important that both parts are the same size. In addition to highlighting Emily's current understanding, this clinical interview also revealed a potential issue of access, specifically with the area-model representation of 1/2. Emily's representation of 1/2 involved *halving* a shape, rather than representing the quantity 1/2. When asked about her drawing, she explained that the entire shape was the representation of "one," rather than understanding the 1 in 1/2 as one of the two parts. The numerals 1 and 2 in the representation of one-half were therefore mapped onto the *one* shape, which was then cut into *two* parts. Emily's nonconventional representation of 1/2 was somewhat surprising because research has shown that even young children have an intuitive understanding of 1/2 (Empson 1999; Empson and Turner 2006; Hunting and Sharpley 1988). Emily's nonconventional drawing and explanation of 1/2 suggests that area models might not serve as a meaningful way for her to represent fractions.

Table 3.1. Emily represents the fraction 1/2

Transcript	Features of clinical interview
Interviewer: If you were to close your eyes and imagine the fraction one-half, what would you think of?	Asks the student an open-ended question.
Student: Half.	
Interviewer: Half? Can you sort of draw or write what you are thinking of?	Encourages student to make her thinking visible.
Student: Yeah, Want me to?	
Interviewer: I'd love you to. You can also just describe it, whatever works for you.	
Student: [*draws circle and partitions it into two; see fig. 3.1*]	
Interviewer: Is there any other way to draw or write it?	Asks student to explain her answer.
Student: Um hmm. [*writes 1/2; see fig. 3.1*]	
Interviewer: Can you explain to me how these two things that you have written out are one-half?	Asks student to explain her answer.
Student: Well, this is one [*traces around the circle*] and it's cut in half, and there is two of the exact same [*points back and forth between pieces*]—I mean, they are not the exact same, but they are supposed to be the exact same size.	
Interviewer: OK, and what about this one? [*points to 1/2*]	
Student: It's one over two. So, it's like, it's just that. [*points to 1/2*]	

On another occasion, I asked Emily to draw the fraction 3/5 (see fig. 3.2). Although she drew a correct representation of 3/5, she began to refer to her own drawing as 2/5. See table 3.2.

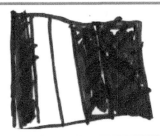

Fig. 3.2. Emily's drawing of 3/5

Table 3.2. Emily represents the fraction 3/5

Transcript	Features of clinical interview
Interviewer: OK, so if we were going to draw a picture of three-over-five, what would it look like?	Asks open-ended question. (I used the phrase "three-over-five" to be consistent with how the student referred to fractions previously.)
Student: [*draws picture of 3/5; see fig. 3.2*]	
Interviewer: Cool.	
Student: It's two-over-five. Wait! Yeah.	
Interviewer: So this is two-over-five?	Echoes back student's answer.
Student: Uh huh.	
Interviewer: Why is that two-over-five?	Asks student to explain her answer.
Student: Because, because these [*points to unshaded parts; see fig. 3.2*] are the ones that are left.	
Interviewer: What do you mean by "left"?	Asks student to further elaborate on her meaning.
Student: They're not shaded in.	
Interviewer: So what does that tell us that they are not shaded in? Why is it important that these two aren't shaded in?	
Student: Because . . . I don't know.	
Interviewer: So what is this a picture of?	Rephrases question.
Student: Three-over-five, right?	
Interviewer: OK, so it's a picture of three-over-five, and we know that it is three-over-five, how?	Asks student to explain her new answer.
Student: There are five pieces, and then I sha— and then I, wait, yeah. I shaded in three pieces and then there's five.	

Again, in this example, I used one open-ended question and several follow-up questions to help me learn about Emily's understanding of her area-model representation of 3/5. Emily drew a valid representation of 3/5 (see fig. 3.2), and her drawing suggests that she understood that it was not essential for all shaded pieces to be contiguous. However, immediately after drawing this representation, she identified her own drawing of 3/5 as 2/5. She focused on the two pieces that were not shaded, which she referred to as the amount "left." After several follow-up questions, Emily changed her answer and tentatively decided that her drawing was a picture of "three-over-five." At this point, I wanted to probe a bit more into Emily's understanding of her drawing of 3/5. I rephrased this question using the conventional fraction term *three-fifths* and attempted to determine if considering the area model as a picture of a cake would support her interpretation of her drawing. See table 3.3.

Table 3.3. Emily reconsiders the fraction 3/5

Transcript	Features of clinical interview
Interviewer: So if this was cake [*points to drawing of 3/5; see fig. 3.2*], we were talking about three-fifths of a cake. Which parts would still be cake, at the end?	Asks question with a context.
Student: These ones. [*pointing to the two unshaded pieces of the area model of 3/5; see fig. 3.2*]	
Interviewer: OK.	
Student: Right?	
Interviewer: And it's those ones, why?	
Student: I don't know. Because they are not shaded in. I don't know. Do you want me to draw you a cake? [*draws circular shape and partitions into five parts; see fig. 3.3*] So now [*coloring in pieces*] 1, 2, 3. There's two left.	Rather than answering her question about the correctness of her answer, I ask the student to explain her answer.

Fig. 3.3. Emily's second drawing of 3/5

Although Emily drew two valid representations of the fraction $3/5$ (figs. 3.2 and 3.3), she interpreted her drawing in terms of the unshaded pieces. In each case, she described these pieces as "left," which may suggest that she understood the shading to be a removal of pieces rather than a signifier of the fractional quantity. In both instances, she interpreted the fractional quantity ($3/5$) she had drawn as the fractional complement ($2/5$). This response suggests that area models are not stable representations of quantity for Emily and provides additional evidence that this representational tool was at least partially inaccessible for Emily.

These clinical interviews revealed that Emily understood area model representations of fractions in atypical ways. This information was critically important for me because I planned how to teach more complex fraction concepts, such as equivalence and fraction operations. If I were to rely on an area model of $1/2$ to introduce a concept such as fraction equivalence, Emily could struggle because she might be thinking of the act of *halving a shape* as opposed to the quantity one-half. Similarly, if I were to use area models to introduce fraction addition, her tendency to interpret area models in terms of the fractional complement could lead to issues. Having identified these atypical ways of understanding area models during my clinical interviews with Emily, I could anticipate the difficulties she might have and consider alternative instructional approaches to provide her with access to the same mathematical ideas.

Instructional Implications

The clinical interview suggested that area models alone did not serve as an accessible representation of fractional quantity. Therefore, instruction should support Emily's understanding of this representational tool through additional supports. To provide Emily with access to this representation it may be beneficial to connect these representations to real-life quantities (Lamon 1996). For example, using a student's experience with physical magnitudes such as length, weight, and temperature can help the student understand representations of quantity (Saxe et al. 2010). Because Emily had difficulties understanding the focal fractional quantity and sometimes paid attention to the amount left (e.g., fractional complement), it may also be necessary to routinely ground discussion of fractions with respect to the whole (Mack 2000). Starting with a physical whole that can be partitioned and physically manipulated may provide Emily with greater access to and understanding of area model representations. Much of special education literature emphasizes the importance of using these kinds of concrete manipulatives with students with different abilities (e.g., Witzel 2005). It may also be beneficial to allow Emily to continue using these supports even after they are no longer necessary for most other students in the class.

As with all mathematics, learning the content and concepts involves understanding the conventions used with various mathematical representations. Explicit class discussions should explore conventions for area models and how they are used. However, I want to caution against decontextualized teaching of conventions. We do not want to teach Emily a prescriptive way of interpreting these representations. Mathematical representations are intended to serve as tools for mathematical meaning making. Teaching a procedural approach for drawing or interpreting representations turns the representation itself into a procedure to be memorized and robs it of its value as a tool for making meaning. When designing instructional approaches for Emily, the goal is to help her gain access to ways of representing and reasoning about fractional quantities, not for her to develop rote ability to draw representations in conventional ways. Attempting to simply ensure that she knows the steps for drawing and interpreting area models may simply mask the underlying issue rather than truly provide her with access to the concepts. Therefore, the instructional objective should remain mathematical meaning making, rather than procedural adherence to particular arbitrary conventions.

Embedded within these instructional recommendations is an intentional attempt to modify the student's access to the content while maintaining the mathematical rigor (Lynch, Hunt, and Lewis, in press). It is critical that students with different abilities have the opportunity to engage in rigorous mathematics. In many ways, high-quality mathematics instruction for students with different abilities is fundamentally the same as high-quality mathematics instruction for students with typical abilities. The goal is to build on students' prior understanding and help them meaningfully engage in rich mathematics. Therefore, instruction for Emily should build on her understanding of the equality of the parts comprising the whole and, potentially, her ability to see both the fractional quantity and the fractional complement within one representation. Clinical interviews are a powerful tool that enables teachers to assess a student's current understanding and aspects of difference, which may render otherwise high-quality instruction less accessible for particular students.

As it was with Emily, a clinical interview with Ryan would be a helpful first step for Ms. Fuentes to investigate how he understands mathematics and why he is experiencing difficulties. Ms. Fuentes could focus this interview on a wide range of topics to get an overall sense of his mathematical understanding or, as in the interview with Emily, focus on a specific mathematical topic. This clinical interview will highlight his current understanding and ways in which he may understand representations in different ways and will help identify potential issues of access that should be accounted for as Ms. Fuentes considers how to design differentiated instruction for him.

Although I have offered some suggestions for how one might assess and then modify instruction to increase access, this approach is neither straightforward nor easily implemented. Equity-oriented teaching is a journey, not a destination. To provide equitable classrooms, teachers must continuously monitor potential issues of access. (See chapters 8 and 9 for other ways to monitor issues of access in the mathematics classroom.) Using the clinical interview can provide insight into the ways in which taken-for-granted representations might be problematic for particular students. This knowledge can meaningfully inform instructional decisions and help reach students who are struggling for unknown reasons.

Reflecting and Taking Action

Although expertise in clinical interviewing develops over time, Ginsburg (1997) provides a few simple guidelines that can be used to help you successfully implement your first clinical interview. This section outlines general guidelines for preparing for and conducting a clinical interview to assess the student's current mathematical understanding and the accessibility of specific tools.

First, before the interview, assemble a set of materials to enable the student to make his or her thinking visible (manipulatives, pen, and paper) and generate a set of open-ended questions and follow-up probes to guide the interview. Although any open-ended question can be used, I recommend deliberately phrasing the questions to minimize the focus on the correctness of the answer and to highlight the focus on student thinking. Boaler and Humphreys (2005) recommend that teachers never ask a question to which they know the answer. For example, rather than ask the question "What is 5 + 9 = ?" it is better to ask, "How would you solve the problem 5 + 9 = ?" because the interviewer will legitimately not know the answer to that question. Phrasing the question in this way reinforces the idea that the student is the expert in this context. To assess the accessibility of different mathematical tools (e.g., drawings and manipulatives), ask the student to represent and interpret various quantities using those tools. When deciding on the sequencing of questions, I recommend starting with a question that you are confident the student can answer relatively easily. Starting in this way gives the student an opportunity to practice sharing his or her thinking on a topic that he or she feels comfortable with.

Second, at the start of the interview, establish the "rules of the game" for the student (Ginsburg 1997). It is important to help the student know that this is a different kind of interaction than she or he typically has with a teacher. For example, I might say, "I am going to ask you a bunch of different kinds of mathematics questions to learn how you think, so I can be a better teacher. It's not important whether an answer is right or wrong; I want to understand how you are thinking about the mathematics. You are the expert, because only you know how you think. To help me understand, I'm going to ask you to explain how you got your answers and to show me how you figured them out." Because students often look to their teachers for feedback and guidance, this expectation setting is particularly important. By setting these expectations in this way, you can work collaboratively with students to explore their mathematical understanding.

Third, during the interview, actively listen to the student and encourage the student to make his or her thinking visible in whatever way he or she can. Pay close attention to the student's words, actions, and gestures, because each of these provides a window into the student's thinking. When you are unsure of what the student said or meant, echo back to the student what you saw or heard to give him or her an opportunity to clarify. For example, you can say, "So you said [*echo back what student said*]. Did I get that right?" or "I saw that you [*describe what the student draw or wrote*]. Can you explain why you did that?" One final technique often used in clinical interviews is "counter-suggestion" (Ginsburg 1997). A counter-suggestion can be used when a student has answered a question *correctly* but is having trouble elaborating on her or his thinking. You can say, for example, "Another student I was working with solved this problem like this [*incorrect answer*]. What do you think of that?" Asking the student to consider another answer will often enable her or him to justify her or his own answer more fully and will give you insight into the student's thinking.

Ginsburg (1997) also offers general guidelines about what to avoid during clinical interviews. First, throughout the interview, avoid giving feedback on the accuracy of a student's answers. Be conscious of your facial expression, body language, and tone of voice, and try to respond in the same way if the student provided a correct answer or an incorrect one. If a student asks whether the answer is correct, you can redirect the student to explain his or her reasoning or remind him that you are more interested in his or her thinking rather than the accuracy of specific answers. It is, however, good to provide encouragement and to praise the student's effort and participation. You can say, "You are doing a really great job explaining your thinking" or "I know I am asking really difficult questions. You are doing a great job explaining how you are thinking through the mathematics." The student's success in the clinical interview ultimately should be based on whether he or she was able to use words, drawings, and manipulatives to help you understand how he or she is thinking about a problem.

Second, Ginsburg (1997) recommends avoiding the inclination to teach. As teachers, we want to help our students correct errors they might make. Indeed, teachers may feel uncomfortable ending the clinical interview with the student having said something that was mathematically inaccurate. However, engaging in teaching within the clinical interview is a violation of the expectations you established with your student. It is much better to take that information and figure out how to address that misunderstanding at another time. The clinical interview is an opportunity to gather a wealth of information about your student's thinking, and switching to teaching mode can undermine the interview and the expectations you set with the student.

Principles to Actions: Ensuring Mathematical Success for All (NCTM 2014) calls for all students to have access to high-quality mathematics instruction. In this chapter, I argue that, particularly for students with different abilities, not only do we need to think about providing the opportunity to be exposed to this kind of instruction, but we also need to critically assess the accessibility of the instruction itself. I provided a description, guidelines, and examples of how a clinical interview can be used to assess student's prior knowledge and identify potential issues of access (see chapter 2 for more examples of interviews with students). These one-on-one interviews can directly influence the design of differentiated instruction, which provides students with different abilities alternative ways to access the same rich mathematics content. Although this clinical interviewing approach can be used with all students, it is particularly appropriate for working with students with different abilities, because these students may experience unique issues of access. Assessing and acknowledging these students' differences is a first step toward providing instruction that is truly accessible to all.

Acknowledgments

This chapter was supported by the Diversity in Mathematics Education grant No. ESI-0119732 from the National Science Foundation. The opinions expressed are those of the author and do not represent views of the National Science Foundation. I would like to thank Emily, for generously sharing her time and thinking with me.

References

Boaler, Jo, and Cathy Humphreys. *Connecting Mathematical Ideas: Middle School Video Cases to Support Teaching and Learning.* Portsmouth, N.H.: Heinemann Educational Books, 2005.

Empson, Susan. B. "Equal Sharing and Shared Meaning: The Development of Fraction Concepts in a First-Grade Classroom." *Cognition and Instruction* 17, no. 3 (1999): 283–342.

Empson, Susan. B., and Erin Turner. "The Emergence of Multiplicative Thinking in Children's Solutions to Paper Folding Tasks." *Journal of Mathematical Behavior* 25, no. 1 (2006): 46–56. doi:10.1016/j.jmathb.2005.11.001

Ginsburg, Herbert P. *Entering the Child's Mind: The Clinical Interview in Psychological Research and Practice.* New York: Cambridge University Press, 1997.

Hunting, Robert P., and Christopher F. Sharpley. "Fraction Knowledge in Preschool Children." *Journal for Research in Mathematics Education* 19, no. 2 (1988): 175–80.

Jackson, Kara, Lynsey Gibbons, and Charlotte Dunlap. "Teachers' Views of Students' Mathematical Capabilities: Challenges and Possibilities for Ambitious Reform." *Teachers College Record* 119, no. 7 (2017): 1–43.

Karp, Karen. "The Invisible 10%: Preparing Teachers to Teach Mathematics to Students with Special Needs." Presentation at the Association of Mathematics Teacher Educators Annual Conference, Orlando, Florida, 2013.

Lamon, Susan J. "The Development of Unitizing: Its Role in Children's Partitioning Strategies." *Journal for Research in Mathematics Education* 27 (1996): 170–93. doi:10.2307/749599

Lewis, Katherine E. "Difference Not Deficit: Reconceptualizing Mathematical Learning Disabilities." *Journal for Research in Mathematics Education* 45, no. 3 (2014): 351–96. doi:10.5951/jresematheduc.45.3.0351

Lynch, Sararose D., Jessica H. Hunt, and Katherine E. Lewis. "Productive Struggle for All: Differentiated Instruction." *Mathematics Teaching in the Middle School* 23, no. 4 (2018): 194–201.

Mack, Nancy K. "Long-Term Effects of Building on Informal Knowledge in a Complex Content Domain: The Case of Multiplication of Fractions." *Journal of Mathematical Behavior* 19, no. 3 (2000): 307–32. doi:10.1016/S0732-3123(00)00050-X

National Council of Teachers of Mathematics (NCTM). *Principles to Actions: Ensuring Mathematical Success for All*. Reston, Va.: NCTM, 2014.

Saxe, Geoffrey B., Darrell Earnest, Yasmin Sitabkhan, Lina C. Haldar, Katherine E. Lewis, and Ying Zheng. "Supporting Generative Thinking about the Integer Number Line in Elementary Mathematics." *Cognition and Instruction* 28, no. 4 (2010): 433–74. doi:10.1080/07370008.2010.511569

Van Garderen, Delinda, Amy Scheuermann, Christa Jackson, and David Hampton. "Supporting the Collaboration of Special Educators and General Educators to Teach Students Who Struggle with Mathematics: An Overview of the Research." Special issue, *Building Systems to Support Students at Risk for Failure in Schools* 46, no. 1 (2009): 56–77. doi:10.1002/pits.20354

Vygotsky, Lev Semenovic. *The Fundamentals of Defectology (Abnormal Psychology and Learning Disabilities)*. Vol. 2 of *The Collected Works of L. S. Vygotsky*. Translated by Jane E. Knox and Carol B. Stevens; edited by R. W. Rieber and A. S. Carton. New York: Plenum Press, 1993.

Wilhelm, Annie G., Charles Munter, and Kara Jackson. "Examining Relations between Teachers' Diagnoses of Sources of Students' Difficulty in Mathematics and Students' Opportunities to Learn." *Elementary School Journal* 117, no. 3 (2017: 345–70.

Witzel, Bradley S. "Using CRA to Teach Algebra to Students with Math Difficulties in Inclusive Settings." *Learning Disabilities: A Contemporary Journal* 3, no. 2 (2005): 49–60.

CHAPTER 4

Balancing Acts

Design-Based Mathematics for Students Living with Trauma

Maria del Rosario Zavala, *San Francisco State University*

Marianna Singwi-Ferrono, *Roses in Concrete Community School, Oakland, California*

A small group of fourth-grade students huddles around a map of their school's future fifth-grade outdoor space. The map is produced on grid paper and sits in front of a large piece of paper with a four-column chart labeled "surface," "square yards," "fraction," and "purpose." As they talk, they gesture toward the paper, tracing lines on the map with pencils and markers. The energy level is high, as students encourage one another's ideas:

"So what do we want to do with this space?"

"I think we should make a hangout zone, or wait maybe—"

"And a stage, but—"

"Maybe it'll be smaller than that," chimes in another student, tapping the map and gesturing with her hands, holding them about shoulder width apart.

"I don't want the stage area to be too big, but wait—oh oh oh! I got it! Maybe this part could be the stage, and this part the audience?" a student asks, tracing a straight line through the group's largest open space on their map.

"But wait, we don't want to make it indoor, we really want it outdoor."

"Yeah," they all agree, "outdoor."

As the discussion continues, the three students write down on the chart their ideas for the kinds of surfaces they need. They get up from their seats and visit the class's paper representation of one square yard taped on the ground, asking one another, "Do we think 15 square yards is big enough?" They discuss how much space they need for each area, what kind of surface they would want (grass, asphalt, turf, wood, etc.), and calculate the fraction of the total area of the outdoor space by using a previously calculated number of total square yards.

The students in this group are focused and energetic. The buzz around the room is electric. Although the adults (the authors) are closely monitoring the groups having difficulties for extra support, most students in the class are working on translating their ideas for their outdoor space into mathematical measurements. This is the kind of engagement we were hoping for.

Making a Commitment to Access and Equity

The students in this vignette are working through a multiday design project, applying mathematical concepts to decide how to design and divide up the school's outdoor space. But this is not an advanced mathematics class; rather, this is a regular classroom in an East Oakland, California, community school. Roses in Concrete Community School, affectionately known as "Roses," was founded in August 2015. At the time of this writing, its student population is approximately two hundred: 50 percent African American and 45 percent Latino, with 5 percent falling outside those demographics, including non-Hispanic white, Pacific Islander, Native American, Asian, and Indian backgrounds. In its first year, Roses served students from kindergarten through fourth grade and planned to add one grade level per year, providing education for kindergartners through twelfth graders by 2024.

Roses was named for a book of poetry, *The Rose That Grew from Concrete* by Tupac Shakur (1999). The school has adopted Shakur's metaphor of the tenacious rose from the title poem, to capture the resilience of Roses' students, who, in the most unforgiving of environments, blossom into beautiful roses. The staff members of Roses are committed to this vision: to educating children who will transform their community into a rose garden. The main goals of Roses are for the children to embody love, honesty, strength of character, and hope, as well as to create a community committed to fighting injustices anywhere (Roses in Concrete 2015). Roses illustrates an educational model for urban schools dedicated to serving the basic needs of children and their families in concert with education. Roses exemplifies how strong and viable communities, in East Oakland or elsewhere, can spring from a modest blacktop.

Many students at Roses could be described as living with trauma. Carter's (2007) research on students' mental health suggests a correlation between oppression and trauma. Carter sees racism as contributing to traumatic stress, suggesting that students may be susceptible to trauma because of their racial identities. On another level, students may experience traumatic events directly. Carlson (1997) offers three criteria for determining whether an event is traumatic: the perception that the event is negative, the suddenness of the event, and a lack of control over the event. The classroom teacher in the vignette (chapter co-author Singwi-Ferrono) was aware of a large number of traumatic events and continuing trauma experienced by many students. Some students had shared traumatic experiences with the class, as part of building community and having a safe space to discuss personal matters. In addition, we (the chapter co-authors) are also aware that many students live in areas of Oakland where they are more likely to experience or witness traumatic events, including violence instigated by police or immigration officers, interrupted home lives (such as being forced to live with unfamiliar relatives or in foster homes), absences of parents for multiple reasons, forced homelessness, the death of a close family member, incarceration of a family member, food insecurities, or knowing someone personally who has experienced these traumas.

We are careful to not assume that every child in Singwi-Ferrono's classroom is living with trauma; however, trauma seems likely to be present within the community. We also want to caution the reader that we do not suggest that design-based mathematics tasks are somehow proved to be therapeutic. Rather, by reflecting on our experience facilitating an open-ended design project and analyzing student work, we seek to better understand how the mathematics curriculum can be tailored to support students with trauma toward mathematical agency. In this chapter, we report on key considerations and outcomes of teaching a play-space design mathematics unit over a five-week period. We share these experiences as a way to encourage and offer insight to other teachers striving for equity in their own classrooms.

There is increased interest among researchers about how traumatic events, or repeated traumatic events, affect student learning. The National Child Traumatic Stress Network reports the following:

A traumatic event can seriously interrupt the school routine and the processes of teaching and learning. There are usually high levels of emotional upset, potential for disruptive behavior, or loss of student attendance unless efforts are made to reach out to students and staff with additional information and services. Students traumatized by exposure to violence have been shown to have lower grade point averages, more negative remarks in their cumulative records, and more reported absences from school than other students. They may have increased difficulties concentrating and learning at school and may engage in unusually reckless or aggressive behavior. (National Child Traumatic Stress Network n.d.)

These outcomes for students with trauma paint a grim picture. They point to a need for a strong stance toward equity for such students to counter traditional outcomes such as low grade-point averages and negative remarks on their records. As NCTM's position statement on Equity and Access notes, "Acknowledging and addressing factors that contribute to differential outcomes among groups of students are critical to ensuring that all students routinely have opportunities to experience high-quality mathematics instruction, learn challenging mathematics content, and receive the support necessary to be successful" (NCTM n.d.).

Thus, students living with trauma must be supported to engage in meaningful mathematics instruction that accounts for the intersections of their experiences, including their cultural ways of knowing, prior learning experiences, and the impact that living with posttraumatic stress or repeated trauma can have on them. They need opportunities to experience mathematical agency, engage in decision making, and see that their mathematical ideas are valuable to others. This in turn affects their sense of having some control over a situation that has an impact on their own learning and provides the opportunity to work in a safe and supported environment with the constant support of peers and teachers.

NCTM's (2014) *Principles to Actions: Ensuring Mathematical Success for All* includes many ideas about how teachers can act on their commitment to access and equity. One that resonated most with our work is the idea that "effective mathematics instruction leverages students' cultures, conditions, and language to support and enhance mathematics learning." (p. 63). The teachers at Roses did this in many ways, but we see particular connections to the project we undertook with children, described in more detail in the next section, because of how it was situated in an authentic problem-solving context.

To us, NCTM's Access and Equity Principle hints at connections to social justice for students in the intermediate grades. First, the struggle for civil rights and education of black and brown students is deeply connected to learning mathematics, as mathematics illiteracy makes them "the designated serfs of the information age" (Moses and Cobb 2001, p. 11), left behind in a world where mathematics literacy is a gatekeeper to high-paying jobs. Second, a key purpose of teaching mathematics for social justice is to critically engage students in the mathematics of their communities, to both interpret social issues through a mathematical lens and use mathematics as a tool to change the conditions of their lives (Gutstein 2006; Turner et al. 2009). For us, the project was situated in a real experience that affected students' lives while also being a platform both for learning classical mathematics (i.e., content standards) and for drawing on community knowledge (Gutstein 2006). Further, when curriculum is a bridge between school and home knowledge, students gain more access to content.

Advancing Access and Equity

Marianna Singwi-Ferrono, the classroom teacher and this chapter's co-author, had been teaching fourth-grade mathematics and Spanish language arts to both sections of fourth-grade students all year. She and the other fourth-grade teacher each taught half of the content areas so that they could work closely with the entire fourth grade. Prior to teaching in Oakland, she taught elementary school in a diverse urban neighboring school district. Maria del Rosario Zavala, the chapter's other co-author, volunteered in Singwi-Ferrono's class once or twice a week and served as a thought partner for designing curriculum as well as an extra support person in the classroom.

Singwi-Ferrono had spent the year developing deep relationships with the students she taught. The school's commitment to being a safe place for students to learn and develop as people falls directly in line with how advocates for students living with trauma perceive school: "School is a place where it is possible for traumatized children to forge strong relationships with caring adults and learn in a supportive, predictable, and safe environment" (Cole et al. 2005, p. 5). Schools are places where students with trauma should feel safe and nurtured, and therefore this dimension of support was not set aside when planning the mathematics task. Rather, these ideas were important to how the design task was structured, as part of a safe, nurturing environment where students' ideas were going to be taken seriously.

The design project began to take shape in April, toward the end of the school year. Singwi-Ferrono knew she wanted students to learn about three topics in the California fourth-grade mathematics standards: areas of polygons, perimeter, and multiplying fractions by whole numbers. She also wanted to do a project where students could continue to work explicitly on how to collaborate well with others, and therefore she wanted something "group worthy" (Featherstone et al. 2011, p. 110). Finally, she was ready to take a break from the curriculum she had been working with and to engage with an open-ended and creative task.

We discussed possible contexts through which to teach these concepts. We kept coming back to the idea of designing a space and making a scaled rendering of the space by using mathematics. Then an opportunity presented itself: The school would be undertaking its first planned expansion over the summer, and an outside area of the school currently off-limits to students would house the new fifth-grade classrooms the following year. Singwi-Ferrono consulted with the architect about the possibility of having the students provide input to the new design, and he was delighted to support this project. With the seed of the idea set, we sketched out roughly what steps students would take to go from brainstorming a design for the space, to using mathematics to determine specific areas and perimeters of planned features of the space, and finally to calculating the fraction of the whole area that each feature occupied. This project would culminate in an illustration of the space, a table (listing the distinct purpose of each area, the square yardage of each area, and the fraction of the total space each area occupied), and a write-up of the process.

In our case, the authenticity of the design project was fortunate. We want to emphasize, however, that in designing the curriculum, we took the opportunity to mathematize the situation and to give students a specific purpose for their projects. Had we not pursued that opportunity, or if the school had decided to postpone its expansion plans, the context would have remained authentic enough for students to see a reason to complete the project. Had the school not been expanding, we would have still used the context of a play-area redesign that used the existing outdoor area of the school. Pursuing the authentic connection was well worth the extra time needed to communicate with the architect.

Goals of the Project

NCTM's *Principles to Actions: Ensuring Mathematical Success for All* states that effective mathematics instruction begins with clear goals, situated within learning progressions (NCTM 2014, p. 12). Before beginning the project, Singwi-Ferrono reflected on her goals for the students. This reflection was important, because we knew from the start that rather than pre-create a unit of materials from scratch, we wanted to set goals for the project and allow ourselves flexibility from day to day. The mathematical goals aligned with California Common Core fourth-grade standards (National Governors Association Center for Best Practices and Council of Chief State School Officers [NGA Center and CCSSO] 2010) and included these:

- Use multiplication to solve real-world problems, including calculating areas of irregular shapes (connected to standard 4.NBT.5 and 4.MD.3).

- Solve problems using conversion of units (connected to 4.MD.1).

- Solve word problems involving a fraction multiplied by a whole number (specifically, using the area formula of a triangle as $\frac{1}{2} \times w \times h$; connected to standard 4.NF.4.C).

In addition, we selected some of the Common Core Mathematical Practice Standards that we wanted to encourage in this project: *Attending to precision* (such as when making a scaled rendering of a space or calculating areas or fractions of areas), *using appropriate tools strategically*, and engaging in a process of *modeling with mathematics* by encouraging multiple iterations of work.

Singwi-Ferrono also wanted students to understand that mathematics has a purpose in their lives and is not just isolated to the classroom—as important to her as the specific mathematics goals. An open-ended design task would be a way for students to experience applied mathematics as well as engage with mathematics alongside their sense of aesthetics and what they would like to see and feel in a space that they would be able to use. The real-world context also gave them experience working with constraints, which in the abstract world of typical school mathematics are frequently minimized for the sake of calculations.

Finally, it was important to Singwi-Ferrono that students learn how to reach compromises as they work together. A large part of building community is helping students learn how to see one another as resources and to counter notions of who the "smart" and "fast" kids are. Some students in the class were also very skilled at putting one another down—in some cases, we suspect, as a self-preservation mechanism for living with trauma. Research has documented that students living with trauma are more likely to act out, even threaten others, either as part of their coping mechanisms or when triggered by stimulus. Therefore, the final goal was to help students self-regulate around the norms that make for positive and effective group collaboration, to provide opportunities for continued growth in self-monitoring alongside the entire school's explicit efforts to build a positive culture.

The goals that Singwi-Ferrono set for the project align with NCTM's Access and Equity Principle. Responsiveness to students' experiences, backgrounds, and ways of knowing were central to this project; and students were encouraged to draw heavily on their desires and experiences in designing their play space. In addition, this project embodied the idea that "effective teaching practices (e.g., engaging students with challenging tasks, discourse, and open-ended problem solving) have the potential to open up greater opportunities for higher-order thinking and for raising the mathematics achievement of all students, including poor and low-income students" (NCTM 2014, p. 63). The open-ended, but teacher-facilitated, nature of the project allowed for students to work through challenging mathematics content while also providing support that each student needed.

Also, given the racial identities in the class, many students could have been seen, stereotypically, as underachieving in mathematics. However, rejecting these stereotypes is key to equity in mathematics, and supporting students to provide counter-stories to persistent patterns of underachievement is also important with students who are traditionally marginalized in mathematics. Typically, underachieving African American and Latino students are seen as lacking basic skills and are fed basic skills through rote practice—the banking model of education that Paolo Freire and others have criticized (Freire 1998). Thus, a key assumption we make of students is that they can be trusted to complete rigorous, open-ended tasks, given the right support.

Key Steps in the Design Project

As we reflect on the experience of facilitating students in this project, we realize that an emphasis on responsive pedagogy, close attention to group dynamics, and setting students up for success characterize how Singwi-Ferrono guided students. We notice an interplay of teacher-led activity with student-led activity—a balancing act of who led the work. Next, we describe the key steps in the five-week project.

Step 1: Teacher launched the task. Students began by brainstorming and using Google Earth to research outdoor spaces in their communities that they loved. The class discussed what elements of the outdoor spaces were most appealing and why, as well as the balance between making spaces both functional and beautiful. Then the class brainstormed what kinds of activities they would like to be able to do in the new outdoor space and how they would like the outdoor space to feel. Students developed a range of purposes for the space, including outdoor recreation, learning, community meeting spaces, performance, gardening, socializing, and cooling down outdoors when upset. The students' intended purposes and feelings of the space drove their designs. Students came to a consensus with their group about how to use the space.

Meanwhile, Singwi-Ferrono began to draw an overhead view of the space that used accurate measurements. Cesar Salgado, another school employee, was instrumental in this process, using his drafting skills to complete the drawing. He created the drawing in a way that would invite students to use known dimensions to figure out areas and perimeters of spaces (see fig. 4.1).

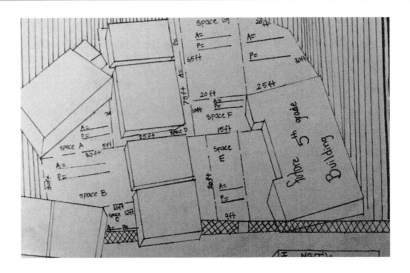

Fig. 4.1. First rendering of the design space (by Cesar Salgado)

Step 2: Teacher facilitated small-group norm setting. In order to work in groups effectively, the class engaged in a variety of agreement-setting activities and community building activities that focused on positive communication and consensus building. Groups were asked to generate agreements that they would stick to. The class also made a list as a whole. At this time, Singwi-Ferrono also made minor adjustments to groups. For example, one group of four was split into two pairs. Using their norms, groups generated open-ended lists of how they would like the space to be used.

Step 3: Teacher led mini-lessons on area and perimeter. Within their design teams, students engaged in learning a variety of mathematical skills that were necessary to create a precise rendering of the outdoor space. First, students calculated the areas and perimeters of the outdoor space they had access to, including rectangular, triangular, and irregular shapes, utilizing the drawing in figure 4.1. Through discussion and exploration, they generated the formulas and methods for finding the area and perimeter of different shapes. They also used estimation in cases where a dimension they needed was missing, and rounding when a space seemed similar to a known polygonal shape.

Step 4: Teacher facilitated mini-investigations into size of square yard. In order to develop a two-dimensional rendering of the space, students needed to convert square feet into square yards. We chose this conversion in order to give students practice in multiplication and division as well as to have them practice with a unit of measurement that might not have been familiar but that can be helpful in describing larger outdoor spaces. After investigating the question "How many square feet are in one square yard?" by measuring and drawing with chalk on the blacktop, the students developed a mathematical process for converting feet to yards and square feet to square yards. At this time, school leadership made a final decision regarding what space fifth-graders would have access to. This information was used to refine the space and make a new two-dimensional drawing for the students to work from (see fig. 4.2).

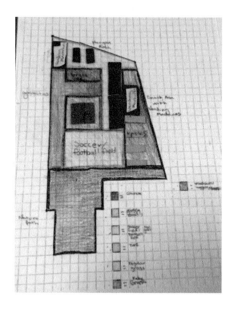

Fig. 4.2. Completed student map, using the two-dimensional template

Step 5: Students led design work on outdoor space. Students decided what fraction of the whole outdoor area they wanted to dedicate to each purpose and the square yardage it would take up. Then they decided what kind of surface (such as grass, blacktop, dirt, sand) that they wanted to cover each area. Students used estimation and measuring skills to make these determinations and drew on personal experiences, as well as new knowledge of how big a square yard is, to make decisions about the area of various shapes within the given space. Finally, with a new rendering of the space to concentrate on, they set out to design the play space by using square yards as a unit of measurement.

Step 6: Teacher led mini-lesson on areas of irregular polygons. Students learned how to classify angles, lines, and quadrilaterals so that they could decide what geometric features they wanted to use on top of the surface areas (e.g., "I want a trapezoid-shaped stage and rectangular tables."). They then decided how much space each of these objects would take up, along with their dimensions, by measuring, estimating, and researching.

Step 7: Guest speaker engaged students in aesthetic considerations. The school's architect engaged students in an interactive presentation about design, reminding students of aesthetic design considerations, as well as of the practical design considerations that architects make. He also reminded students of the importance of balancing aesthetics with function and reminded them of the significance of the work they were undertaking.

Step 8: Students worked in groups on to-scale rendering. Students worked with a square-centimeter-grid paper template to create a final rendering of their design maps. They colored each area and created a key to represent the different materials. They cut out foam to represent the area the objects (tables, swings, stages) would take up, attending to the precise dimensions and measuring with rulers to preserve the scale of one centimeter for every one yard.

Step 9: Students quantified areas from their maps. At this stage, students engaged in the majority of the formal quantification work for the project. They created a table to capture the square yardage, perimeter, and fraction of the total space each area of their map took up. This step required a lot of calculation. During this step we also saw some of the most productive group work happening, as students analyzed their maps section by section and supported each other in the calculation process.

Step 10: Students wrote reflections. Before assembling a final poster of their product, students wrote an explanation of their vision, their map, and their process and reflected on their experiences. Students were given the option to write as a group or to write their own reflections. This modification provided some students with more voice in the project, as individual reflections revealed perspectives that may have been lost in group products. Providing the option, though, was a way to support student preference.

Step 11: Final product assembled and shared. The students edited and finalized their reflections, then created posters displaying their maps, tables, and essays. These posters were displayed at STEM Day and were displayed in the classroom for the rest of the year. During STEM Day, groups of students from other grade levels circulated through the class and took a gallery walk among the posters (see fig. 4.3).

These steps were not planned concretely in advance. The open-ended task and the goals were conceptualized before the project began, but many of the steps were created as the students engaged in the design process. This approach is related to what is known in science inquiry as "activity before concept" (Konicek-Moran and Keeley 2015), an idea also popular in a constructivist approach to teaching mathematics: students should try something out, creating the conditions for learners to need to know something (Wheatley 1991). For example, though at each step Singwi-Ferrono had a hand in facilitating the lesson, she reserved teacher-led mini lessons of the specific required skills before students would need to apply the skill, such as step 3. In this way, students were primed to engage in the lesson, since they had arrived at a point in their planning where they now needed to understand, for example, the actual size of the sections they were trying to divide their play area into by using a measure like square yards (step 4). In traditional skills-based teaching, skills are "front-loaded," practiced, and applied in later lessons. Instead, mathematics skills were integrated into the project as students needed them.

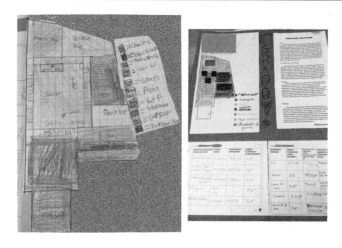

Fig. 4.3. Examples of final projects: Jamal's group's final map (right); a complete poster (right)

Reflecting and Taking Action

In our role as the primary facilitators of the project, we saw clear positive results in students' ability to reason mathematically in a particular context (i.e., planning how to use the outdoor space) and also in their socio-emotional development in how they worked together. We also noticed that the project sustained constructive engagement from some students who typically had trouble focusing, because they were genuinely interested in people hearing their ideas and in hearing what others had to say.

As may be expected in many intermediate classrooms, some patterns of interaction among students sometimes derailed the work. But this project also created some of the longest periods of productive group engagement for students that year. We were encouraged to see the sustained engagement in the activity.

For some students with higher learning needs, this project created space for them to transform relationships with class members and to take a productive role instead of an adversarial or disruptive one. Jamal (pseudonym) was an African American student who frequently had challenges in interacting productively with others. He sometimes fought on the playground, but through the support of the classroom community was learning to express his feelings in productive ways and to take measures to self-regulate. He could pour himself into hands-on activities that held value for him. The design project held his attention in ways that other tasks did not during the school year. Figure 4.3 shows a picture of his group's final plan. In his reflection, Jamal described enjoying the task outside where students used a square-foot cutout to construct a square yard and to determine how many square feet are in a square yard. We noticed that Jamal was proud of the work that he accomplished and that he also reflected on his ability to take more leadership in future design projects. He mentioned the time they got to "do square yards," which was the outdoor exploration on constructing a square yard from a square foot with chalk. He wrote:

> My favorite part about the project was when we had got to color.
> We really liked when we had got to do [square] yards. This project
> is important because people really want this to happen. We learned
> how to do a design project. We learned about yards. One challenge my
> group had was doing the yards because we did not get it. Next time I
> would write a lot more. I hope that the things we wrote can come true.

In terms of agency, we noticed that students seemed to take on ownership of ideas, and they shared the responsibility of figuring out problems. Though at times the teacher needed to intervene with groups and help them remember and apply their group norms, students spent much time productively engaging in group work. Especially during the creation of the square yardage tables, we noticed a lot of groups huddling, helping one another calculate the numbers.

Working in groups with group norms was a positive experience for the students. This does not happen naturally, and the research into small-group work concurs with the idea that teachers must actively facilitate productive small-group work (Cohen and Lotan 1997; Featherstone et al. 2011). (For more strategies that support productive pair work and group work, see chapters 8 and 9). Our willingness to accept flexible grouping was key for our students. Sometimes, teachers feel that changes after group work has started would single out particular students. However, we note that small adjustments, such as moving students into new groups, should be an option if it seems like a positive decision. Separating students punitively for being off topic is perhaps not as good a reason as splitting a foursome into two pairs because one student was overwhelmed trying to participate in a group that size. In the end, there were groups of two, three, and four.

Singwi-Ferrono knew that she needed to be attentive to small-group dynamics and to help students develop and use norms so that every member could feel safe and heard. By prioritizing attention to social dynamics alongside the mathematics, she had success in supporting groups to work together. It took time—and some small-group conferences to give students the support that they needed. For example, in one small group, a student who had trouble engaging with her group sometimes actively aggravated group members or ignored them entirely. Because of the emphasis on working together and the careful selection of group members, she was in a group with students who called a conference with the teacher to talk about how to help her be a productive part of the group. For the rest of the project, the other group members actively worked to include her while respecting that at times she needed space to work away from the group. Many students also wrote in their reflections that they wanted to improve on working with others in groups.

The value and success of this project lies in the realization that no mathematics learning happens in a vacuum. The most powerful lessons are anchored in some kind of context where students see a reason for the learning that takes place. We asserted at the beginning of the chapter that NCTM's Access and Equity Principle demands that all students, including students who live with trauma, have access to mathematics that allows them to feel powerful, confident, and valued and that their ideas are applicable to situations they care about. As the chapter title suggests, such projects may require that teachers balance leading the project with students leading the work.

We also want to underscore the authenticity of the project. True, the timing of the project was opportune. However, had the opportunity not been there, we would have selected a different local context to mathematize (perhaps even sticking with a school-area design project or a design-your-ultimate-classroom project). Authentic opportunity for action is meaningful in teaching for equity, perhaps even more so for intermediate students who are rapidly developing ideas about whether they like mathematics or not and who will decide as early as middle school whether they will pursue studying science or mathematics in the future. We encourage teachers to privilege mathematizing a real situation within the students' local community if your prescribed published curriculum does not have such an opportunity. This is especially important in grades 3–5, because multistep problem solving and the emphasis on measurement and data are explicitly developed in this grade band. In these grades, the toolbox is wider, so teachers can design mathematics tasks that are more accessible and interesting to their students.

The design project described in this chapter, though longer and driven by student ideas, fit into the culture of doing mathematics that Singwi-Ferrono had been working on throughout the year. She had been encouraging a culture of promoting thinking over answers and emphasizing good thinking as a valuable resource. Though some students challenged these ideas in favor of the traditional notion of the importance of "right answers," Singwi-Ferrono drew on the message she had conveyed throughout the year as part of the pedagogy of the design project, which we believe helped students to dream big and generate their own ideas.

Finally, reflecting on the design project led us to think more deeply about how mathematics curriculum can be a step toward healing for students with trauma. Ginwright (2015) notes that healing, along with hope, is an essential trait on the path from surviving to thriving in urban communities affected by multiple traumas. Building on this statement, we reflect on how agency, empowering students to have a say in how they give back to their communities through something like a community-based design project, can be seen as a healing process by giving children a sense of influence on and a little bit of control over how they apply mathematical ideas to the world around them.

We conclude with some final advice for teachers. First, this work is time-consuming but worthwhile. With design-based projects, it is important to keep in mind that you may do a lot of planning up front, but then the children start to take the lead in their work and you are free to support them as they work in groups. Singwi-Ferrono noted that teaching through the design project felt more relaxing than typical lessons, perhaps because the students did a lot of self-directed work, which freed her to monitor and support them. Being able to step off the stage and immerse herself in the work her students were doing required a different kind of energy, one that she welcomed. Planning was frequently about reflecting on the work and its direction and scaffolding the work: many fewer worksheets, much less pressure to move through curriculum. When students are engaged, teachers have more energy because students have more energy.

Second, work with a partner or team: a grade-level partner, a close-grade-level partner, or a coach. Singwi-Ferrono was able to bounce ideas off Zavala, which was helpful when thinking through steps of the project and in keeping the project from going in too many directions. Working collaboratively on just the between-lesson planning also created accountability. As teachers, we should also feel that we have permission to work through an open-ended unit in a way that works for each of us. You do not always need to know that next step; but if you attend closely to the work of your students, you are headed in the right direction.

And finally, trust the students and give them tools. Of all the messages we have for attending to the Access and Equity Principle with intermediate students with trauma, we especially hope that you take away that when you trust students to do the work they will rise to meet your expectations, *if they see the purpose* and if *you commit to supporting them*. We supported students in a variety of ways, such as through the teacher's mini-lessons, in order to give students access to mathematics concepts and skills necessary to continue their own projects. As students worked in groups, we also committed to facilitating group norms and helping groups work through conflict. Even when you feel lost in the weeds of the project, know that you can step back and plan a structured math lesson and then get back to the creative work. Trust that the students can get there with you.

As mathematics teachers, we may not always feel that we have the experience or authority to design mathematics projects that draw heavily on students' ways of knowing and still teach to clear mathematics standards. But, as we have argued and illustrated here, such projects hold potential for a growing group of students in schools who can be identified at the intersection of historically marginalized, urban youth, with trauma. This population should cause us to question if mathematics-as-usual is truly where we should invest our teaching time, or if providing additional opportunities for students to have control over their own learning and connect standards-based mathematics to something meaningful in their lives contributes to a balanced curriculum. We see project-based learning in a relevant context as a strong way for both teachers and students to feel empowered through mathematics.

References

Carlson, Eve. *Trauma Assessments: A Clinician's Guide.* New York: Guildford Press, 1997.

Carter, Robert. "Racism and Psychological and Emotional Injury: Recognizing and Assessing Race-Based Traumatic Stress." *The Counseling Psychologist* 35, no. 1 (2007): 13–105.

Cohen, Elizabeth G., and Rachel A. Lotan. *Working for Equity in Heterogeneous Classrooms: Sociological Theory in Practice.* New York: Teachers College Press, 1997.

Cole, Susan, Jessica Greenwald O'Brien, M. Geron Gadd, Joel Ristuccia, D. Luray Wallace, and Michael Gregory. *Helping Traumatized Children Learn: A Report and a Policy Agenda.* Boston: Massachusetts Advocates for Children, 2005.

Featherstone, Helen, Sandra Crespo, Lisa Jilk, Joy Oslund, Amy Parks, and Marcy Wood. Smarter *Together!: Collaboration and Equity in the Elementary Math Classroom.* Reston, Va.: NCTM, 2011.

Freire, Paolo. *Pedagogy of the Oppressed.* 30th Anniversary edition. New York: Bloomsbury, 1998.

Ginwright, Shawn. *Hope and Healing in Urban Education: How Urban Activists and Teachers Are Reclaiming Matters of the Heart.* New York: Routledge, 2015.

Gutstein, Eric. *Reading and Writing the World with Mathematics: Toward a Pedagogy for Social Justice.* New York: Routledge, 2006.

Konicek-Moran, Richard, and Paige Keeley. *Teaching for Conceptual Understanding in Science.* Arlington, Va.: National Science Teachers Association Press, 2015.

Moses, Robert Parris, and Charles E. Cobb, Jr., *Radical Equations: Civil Rights from Mississippi to the Algebra Project.* Boston, Ma.: Beacon Press, 2001.

National Child Traumatic Stress Network. "The Effects of Trauma on Schools and Learning." n.d. http://www.nctsn.org/resources/audiences/school-personnel/effects-of-trauma

National Council of Teachers of Mathematics (NCTM). *Principles to Actions: Ensuring Mathematical Success for All.* Reston, Va.: NCTM, 2014.

———."Equity and Access in Mathematics Education: A Position of the National Council of Teachers of Mathematics." Standards and Positions, NCTM, Reston, Virginia, n.d. http://www.nctm.org/Standards-and-Positions/Position-Statements/Access-and-Equity-in-Mathematics-Education/

National Governors Association Center for Best Practices and the Council of Chief State School Officers (NGA Center and CCSSO). *Common Core State Standards for Mathematics.* Washington, D.C.: NGA Center and CCSSO, 2010. http://www.corestandards.org.

Roses in Concrete Community School. "Our Mission." Oakland, Calif.: Roses in Concrete, 2015–16. http://rosesinconcrete.org/our-mission/

Shakur, Tupac. *The Rose That Grew from Concrete.* New York: Pocket Books, 1999. (See https://allpoetry.com/The-Rose-That-Grew-From-Concrete for complete poem.)

Turner, Erin E., Maura Varley Gutiérrez, Ksenija Simic-Muller, and Javier Díez-Palomar. "'Everything Is Math in the Whole World': Integrating Critical and Community Knowledge in Authentic Mathematical Investigations with Elementary Latina/o Students." *Mathematical Thinking and Learning* 11, no. 3 (2009): 136–57.

Wheatley, Grayson. "Constructivist Perspectives on Science and Mathematics Learning." *Science Education* 75, no. 1 (1991): 9–21.

CHAPTER 5

Moving the Mathematics Forward while Acquiring English

Zandra de Araujo, *University of Missouri*

Erin Smith, *University of Missouri*

Melanie Kremmel, *Pu'u Kukui Elementary School, Wailuku, Hawaii*

Oksana arrived in Ms. Kremmel's fourth-grade classroom in a small midwestern city about two months after the start of the school year. Oksana's parents were in the United States on business and had planned to stay for about six months. Oksana was a native Russian speaker from Ukraine and had not previously received instruction in English. Ms. Kremmel was a new teacher. She had completed some coursework related to teaching English learners, but her experiences in teaching these learners was limited to several interactions during field experiences. Ms. Kremmel did not speak Russian; and although there were five other English learners in the class, they were not Russian speakers. Thus, Oksana was the sole Russian speaker in the class. The school's EL specialist classified Oksana as a "newcomer," meaning she was new to the United States and to the English language. Oksana's English language proficiency was assessed by using the WIDA Consortium's ACCESS Test and classified at the "entering" level. The ways in which students at the entering level of English proficiency can use English, both receptively and productively, are summarized in figure 5.1 (WIDA Consortium 2011).

	Writing	Speaking
Productive Domains	Draw responses to spoken directions Label objects, images, and diagrams Create images, symbols, and words to communicate	Name objects, people, and pictures Answer questions with choices Answer who, what, or when questions
Receptive Domains	**Reading** Connect symbols and images to words or phrases Identify concepts about print and text features	**Listening** Identify spoken words, phrases, and images Follow spoken, one-step directions Connect spoken statements to objects or images

Fig. 5.1. The WIDA summary of entering English learners' language proficiencies. Adapted from table 5, "PreK–12 CAN DO Descriptors for the Levels of English Language Proficiency," in WIDA Consortium (2011), pp. 22–23. Available at https://www.wida.us/assessment/access/scorereports/access_interpretive_guide11.pdf

Ms. Kremmel worked hard to foster a supportive classroom community and thought it important that Oksana became part of that community. She wanted Oksana to feel welcome in and contribute to the class. Ms. Kremmel was committed to teaching Oksana mathematics with the other students and did not view Oksana's English proficiency as a deficit or as an impediment. Rather, she focused on what Oksana was able to do and went from there. Furthermore, Ms. Kremmel thought it imperative that Oksana's mathematical learning not be put on hold while she acquired the English language. This meant that Ms. Kremmel had to find ways to communicate with Oksana so that she could better understand and build on Oksana's prior mathematical knowledge.

Ms. Kremmel was not provided with information about Oksana's mathematical background, so Ms. Kremmel had to consider ways to learn more about Oksana's mathematical knowledge. Ms. Kremmel's school used an adaptive mathematics software program that focuses on the acquisition of mathematics facts. Because the program consists mainly of visual representations and has low language demands, Ms. Kremmel thought that she could use it to gain information on Oksana's mathematical understandings. Oksana seemed to enjoy the program and quickly surpassed the other students' levels on the program. Within a short time, Oksana was completing middle school content in the software. At the same time, Oksana had earned the highest score on a unit pretest. This information led Ms. Kremmel to consider ways to engage Oksana in mathematics that presented appropriate challenges.

However, Ms. Kremmel also wanted to lessen potential language obstacles; she did not want Oksana's access to mathematics to be limited by unnecessary language demands. Addressing both mathematics and language was a challenge and an opportunity for Ms. Kremmel, which she openly embraced.

Ms. Kremmel wanted to help Oksana engage in appropriate mathematics while also supporting her language development. Unlike many newly arrived English learners, Oksana was not shy or quiet. She would often eagerly raise her hand to present her solution to the class. When she did so, she would write down her solution and then explain her thinking in Russian. In instances such as this, Ms. Kremmel tried to support and encourage Oksana while also attending to her mathematical solution. Over the course of the year, Ms. Kremmel implemented a variety of strategies to help extend Oksana's mathematical thinking without increasing the language demands. Later in this chapter, we describe some of these strategies and resources that Ms. Kremmel found helpful in accomplishing this goal.

Making a Commitment to Access and Equity

Experiences such as Oksana's and Ms. Kremmel's are not uncommon; however, much of the literature related to teaching mathematics with English learners focuses on linguistic support rather than on extending students' mathematical thinking (de Araujo, Smith, and Sakow 2016). Teachers need interconnected strategies in both these areas because students' mathematical learning should not be put on hold while they acquire proficiency in English (e.g., Celedón-Pattichis 2004; Moschkovich 2002; Sigley and Wilkinson 2015). In this chapter, we connect Ms. Kremmel's experiences with Oksana to a broader conversation about the ways in which teachers facilitate the instruction of English learners in elementary grades. In particular, we focus on the ways in which Ms. Kremmel was able to broaden her notion of communication to build on the resources Oksana did have in English rather than focusing on those she did not have. In doing so, Ms. Kremmel was able to help Oksana further her understanding of both mathematics and language.

The increase in the number of English learners in the United States has brought a wealth of cultural and linguistic resources to classrooms and opportunities for teachers to draw on those resources to further broaden the experiences of all students. In order to make the most of these opportunities, teachers must make a commitment to access and equity. In the case of Ms. Kremmel, she strived for equity, not equality, in her classroom. This meant that her goal was "ensuring that all students, regardless of background characteristics, have the same likelihood of achieving meaningful outcomes" (NCTM 2014, p. 60). If Ms. Kremmel had instead aimed for equality, Oksana would have had exactly the same instruction and resources as her peers. Consequently, Oksana, or other English learners in her class, likely would not have had any specific language support. Ms. Kremmel knew that this approach would not help her achieve equity. Ms. Kremmel knew that Oksana needed specific resources and accommodations, different from those given to other students in class, in order to ensure that Oksana had the same opportunities and access to mathematics as the other students.

Ms. Kremmel thought it important to advance Oksana's mathematical learning while she acquired English proficiency. To do this, Ms. Kremmel had to consider ways to provide Oksana access to high-quality mathematics while also facilitating her language development. Commonly, teachers might feel that by following best practices, they are supporting their English learners. Coggins and colleagues challenged this notion:

> if we teach mathematics by following commonly accepted "best practices," we may actually overlook English learners, because they have very specific needs. On the other hand, if we teach mathematics in ways that benefit English learners, then all students will benefit from the rich repertoire of strategies designed to create access to mathematics content. (Coggins et al. 2007, p. ix)

Thus, engagement in best practices is not sufficient in and of itself to achieve equity; teachers must also purposefully enact strategies that support English learners in simultaneously acquiring language and mathematics (Celedón-Pattichis and Ramirez 2012; NCTM 2014).

There is no one-size-fits-all approach to teaching English learners because they are not a homogenous group. Each child enters the classroom with unique experiences and resources from which teachers might draw. This is particularly important to consider when discussing English learners' language and mathematical abilities. In Oksana's case, Ms. Kremmel spent time trying to understand her prior mathematical knowledge so that she could provide the appropriate level of mathematical challenge. This was crucial because a number of studies have found that teachers' attempts to support English learners may result in students receiving mathematics instruction that is highly procedural in nature (e.g., de Araujo 2012, 2017).

In addition to understanding Oksana's prior mathematical knowledge, Ms. Kremmel needed to know more about Oksana's English language abilities in order to build on her existing language and facilitate her access to the language in the curriculum materials. Helping Oksana access the language was important because Ms. Kremmel did not want language to be an obstacle to Oksana's mathematical learning. In thinking of ways to support Oksana, Ms. Kremmel did not assume that she could not understand any English at all. Instead, she took time to talk to and interact with Oksana so that she could more fully understand how to build on what Oksana already knew as she continued to support Oksana's language development. Ms. Kremmel's approach required her to know Oksana's strengths so that she could enact strategies and use resources that would best support Oksana.

Finally, Ms. Kremmel knew that Oksana needed to become a welcomed and contributing member of the classroom community in order to achieve equity. Just as she did with the other students, Ms. Kremmel made sure to acknowledge Oksana's contributions and asked for her input. She did not allow Oksana's English proficiency level to dictate what she could not do; rather, Ms. Kremmel found ways to expand her notion of language to remove obstacles to Oksana's full participation in the class.

Ms. Kremmel held many productive beliefs about access and equity in mathematics. As we illustrate in the following section, these beliefs helped her select resources and enact strategies to support Oksana's access to and engagement in high-quality mathematics.

Advancing Access and Equity

In order to achieve access and equity in the classroom, teachers must facilitate their students' mathematical, communicative, and social competencies (Pinnow and Chval 2014). Mathematical competence includes such aspects as students' knowledge and mastery of mathematical content, mathematical norms (e.g., conventions), and mathematical practices. Said another way, mathematical competence represents all the aspects of mathematics that teachers wish their students to learn. Communicative competence is what teachers typically think of as language. Canale and Swain (1980) defined communicative competence as encompassing grammatical competence (knowing words and rules of grammar), sociolinguistic competence (knowing which rules of discourse to use when), and strategic competence (knowing how to communicate when in unfamiliar situations). In the mathematics classroom, students draw on each of these components, as they must understand not only specific mathematics vocabulary but also the ways in which we explain and justify our thinking and critique the reasoning of others. Finally, social competence refers to the ways that students interact with one another in culturally and socially appropriate ways, including being a productive partner and group member, engaging with peers, and being respectful to others. It is not enough to focus on one or two of these aspects of students' education. In a well-functioning classroom community, the teacher is attending to all three of these competencies.

How teachers position students can greatly affect students' development in these three areas (Pinnow and Chval 2014). "Position" here is metaphorical, not physical, and is related to one's ability to be heard or to contribute to the class (van Langenhove and Harré 1999). In this way, students can be positioned in the classroom as having more or less power and social capital. To illustrate the impact of positioning, consider the following example. Julia's teacher regularly positions her as knowledgeable in her mathematics classroom by frequently calling on her and asking for her mathematical ideas. In contrast, Julia's classmate Luz is rarely asked to speak or share her ideas in class. As a result, the teacher has positioned Luz as a student whose ideas are not worth hearing. Luz was not positioned as capable or valuable; Julia was. As a result of this positioning, Luz becomes quieter and more reserved, whereas Julia continues to eagerly volunteer answers. Though it is not easy, teachers must constantly reflect on the ways in which their actions might position students in ways that have a negative impact on their learning.

When teachers view English learners' language proficiencies as obstacles, teachers may position these students as having less value (Yoon 2008). One of the greatest detriments to English learners who are positioned in this way is the uptake, or mimicking, of such positions by other students (Martin-Beltrán 2010; Turner et al. 2013; Wood 2013; Yoon 2008). As a result, classmates begin to treat English learners as not having the capabilities, proficiencies, and skills needed to actively contribute to the classroom, just as their teacher does. This negative positioning can also affect the identity and the self-efficacy of English learners in detrimental ways (Turner et al. 2013; Wood 2013). In contrast, teachers who position English learners as valuable members of the classroom community are similarly positioned in positive ways by their peers. Ms. Kremmel is one such teacher. In her classroom, as we will discuss, she regularly positioned all students as having resources and skills that were highly valued. This positioning, combined with her focus on mathematical, language, and social competencies, illustrates how Ms. Kremmel increased access and tackled equity head-on in her classroom on a daily basis.

In the following section, we share Ms. Kremmel's story. We discuss in detail the instructional strategies and resources she used over the course of the year that enabled her to achieve her goals of access and equity in mathematics. In particular, we describe how Ms. Kremmel drew on Oksana's prior knowledge bases of language and mathematics, positioned Oksana as a valuable class member, and drew on her family as a resource.

Understanding and Building on Oksana's Prior Knowledge

The school had identified Oksana as a newcomer with English proficiency at the entering level. In many cases, teachers may assume that students such as Oksana cannot understand or communicate in English. Ms. Kremmel did not hold this view. She knew from her prior teacher-preparation coursework that English learners have multiple linguistic resources to draw from. However, Ms. Kremmel had to expand her notion of communication beyond written and spoken English to address the concerns she had for this particular student's access and equity in her mathematics classroom. As a first step to increase access and equity for Oksana, Ms. Kremmel sought out school resources that would help her communicate with Oksana and vice versa. Although Ms. Kremmel's school had an English learner specialist, there were no other speakers of Russian available to support Oksana's transition.

Because her school had limited resources in Russian, Ms. Kremmel used technological resources to translate parts of mathematics tasks for Oksana. The translation software (in this instance, Google Translate) allowed Ms. Kremmel to give Oksana access to some materials in her first language. Ms. Kremmel not only translated materials for Oksana, but she also encouraged Oksana to use the technology to translate for her when needed. The benefit of this is clearly evidenced by this example. Shortly after Oksana entered Ms. Kremmel's class, she was confronted with a situation where her English language proficiency presented itself as an obstacle. While working on a mathematics task, a question arose for Oksana that she was unable to formulate in English. Oksana used technology to translate her question from Russian into English, which Ms. Kremmel was able to understand and address.

The use of the translation software was powerful for Oksana and benefited her in multiple ways. First, she was able to ask her question in a language that she was learning, which enabled her to more fully participate in the classroom than her English language proficiency would allow. In this way, Oksana was not placed in an inequitable situation where her language proficiency was an obstacle that required her to sit back and watch (Pappamihiel 2002). Instead, Ms. Kremmel positioned Oksana's first language as a resource—one that she was expected to draw from. Second, because Oksana was given a translation tool, her access to knowledge was increased. In particular, Ms. Kremmel conveyed that other forms of communication were acceptable in the classroom and that Oksana could draw on them as needed, an approach shown by research to benefit English learners (Chval and Chávez 2012; Moschkovich 2002). Third, Oksana was able to ask higher-order questions than her English proficiency would otherwise allow, allowing Ms. Kremmel to gain a fuller picture of Oksana's mathematical thinking. In addition, this alleviated the stress and frustration that some English learners face when attempting to communicate ideas in content classrooms with entering levels of language proficiency (Yoon 2008). Finally, by providing Oksana access to a language tool that she was expected to use, Ms. Kremmel positioned her as a student who must advocate for herself. Thus, Ms. Kremmel simultaneously attended to Oksana's communicative and social competence.

In addition to making use of technology in the classroom, Ms. Kremmel and Oksana developed other ways to communicate. In particular, they used nonverbal communication, such as gestures, pointing, and body language, to communicate with each other. The WIDA framework (see fig. 5.1) suggests that students at Oksana's level of English proficiency can connect words to images and use images to help respond to questions. Thus, one tool that was particularly helpful in expanding how Oksana communicated was Ms. Kremmel's word wall. The word wall contained mathematics-specific vocabulary and symbols along with graphics. As Oksana would explain her thinking, she would point to different cards on the word wall if she was not sure of the word. Conversely, Ms. Kremmel would point to words to convey her meaning to Oksana. This process allowed the two of them to more effectively communicate by using a resource many elementary teachers have in their classrooms. In addition to using the word wall, Ms. Kremmel commonly asked Oksana to write or draw her thinking so that she could understand Oksana's solution strategy. These strategies helped Oksana access the mathematics and also helped Ms. Kremmel access Oksana's mathematical thinking.

Ms. Kremmel actively sought to solicit Oksana's thinking through multiple modes of communication and enabled her to use these modes to communicate thinking. In this way, Oksana was positioned as a valuable contributor and mathematical thinker in the classroom, regardless of her language proficiency. This move pushed her peers to see beyond one facet of Oksana's identity as a language learner and value other facets as well, such as a mathematical thinker. Moreover, Ms. Kremmel conveyed that language would not be an acceptable shield to hide behind and that all students would be held accountable for participating in the classroom. Over time, as Oksana's English proficiency grew, neither Oksana, Ms. Kremmel, or the class lessened their use of multiple modes of communication. At that point, multiple communication modes had become a classroom norm that was used by all students.

Throughout the year, Ms. Kremmel worked to develop her own understanding of, and to build on, Oksana's existing mathematical and language knowledge. Ms. Kremmel did not assume—as many teachers may—that Oksana had no prior understanding of mathematics or language. Instead, she sought to understand what Oksana already knew. In addition to assessing Oksana's mathematical knowledge in the classroom, Ms. Kremmel used the school district's mathematics education software. This two-pronged approach enabled Ms. Kremmel to gain a more robust understanding of Oksana's prior mathematics knowledge that would have not been possible with just one method. On the basis of this approach, Ms. Kremmel learned that Oksana had a strong mathematical knowledge base from which she could build. This was most evident in her high scores on in-class mathematics unit preassessments and education software progress, which exceeded the scores of her peers. Once Ms. Kremmel had an understanding of Oksana's prior knowledge, she was better able to adapt instruction to effectively challenge her mathematically. In this way, Ms. Kremmel indicated two strong messages to Oksana. First, Oksana should feel challenged in mathematics. Second, Oksana's mathematics education would not take a backseat to language or social education learning. Together, these messages supported Ms. Kremmel's mission to achieve equity and access for all her students. Furthermore, these messages are supported by prior recommendations for guiding principles for teaching mathematics with English learners (Celedón-Pattichis and Ramirez 2012)

Positioning Oksana as a Valuable Member of the Classroom Community

Prior to Oksana's arrival, Ms. Kremmel worked to establish a classroom community that valued student participation, contained meaningful mathematical discussions, and elicited and responded to student thinking. As a teacher, she was aware of how easy it was to create inequitable classrooms for English learners. Ms. Kremmel was familiar with studies that have described problematic practices with regard to English learners' learning. For example, teachers may think that they have to put English learners' content area education on hold while they learn language (Flores, Cousin, and Díaz 1991) and that the peers of English learners can take over and dominate interactions with them, which can limit access to academic content (Pappamihiel 2002). Furthermore, she knew that language proficiency does not prevent class participation by English learners but that the ways in which they are positioned does (Yoon 2008). On the basis of this knowledge, Ms. Kremmel's goal was to position students as competent mathematical problem solvers with valuable contributions, regardless of their language proficiency.

Standing in front of the class, Ms. Kremmel has experienced feelings of uncertainty and uneasiness as she solicited student thinking. Students might ask questions to which she does not know the answer or may take the conversation in a different direction than she had intended (see chapter 2). In addition to these concerns, she has questioned her own ability to manage the classroom conversation with students whose English proficiencies vary. As she considered her classroom conversations, she was not certain how to ensure that Oksana could access the discussion and also feel as though she could contribute. Such feelings are not unique to Ms. Kremmel; many teachers experience similar fears. Conscious of her own uncertainty, Ms. Kremmel pushed herself to consider ways that Oksana could fully participate in class.

A notable instance occurred shortly after Oksana joined the classroom. After students had worked in small groups on problem solving, Ms. Kremmel asked students to share their thinking with the class. In response, Oksana excitedly raised her hand to volunteer. At this point, Ms. Kremmel was faced with a dilemma: Should she call on Oksana, knowing that she might not have the full English-language capabilities to explain her thinking? If she does call on her, how will she ensure that the class understands Oksana's ideas? Considering her goals of access and equity, Ms. Kremmel did not succumb to her own fear and deny Oksana the opportunity to learn and contribute to the classroom conversation, so she called on her.

When invited to share her solution at the board, Oksana surprised Ms. Kremmel. In front of the class, Oksana explained how she thought about and solved the problem, just as any other student would—but entirely in Russian, which no one else in the class spoke. Instead of quickly agreeing with Oksana's explanation, as many teachers might have done, Ms. Kremmel took time to question and clarify Oksana's thinking by drawing on Oksana's English abilities. Drawing on language strategies available to Oksana (as suggested by the WIDA framework; see fig. 5.1), Ms. Kremmel restated her interpretation of Oksana's ideas in simple sentences as she gestured to what Oksana had drawn. To clarify and confirm the accuracy of her summary, Ms. Kremmel asked simple yes-or-no questions to Oksana. Throughout this process, the rest of the class listened and responded just as they would to any other student.

This single classroom event had multiple ramifications. First, by allowing Oksana to participate in the lesson by sharing her solution, Ms. Kremmel positioned her as a valid member of the classroom community who had valuable mathematical ideas that were worth discussing, regardless of the language in which they were communicated (Celedón-Pattichis and Ramirez 2012). Second, Ms. Kremmel relayed to the class that language is a resource to draw from. This move by Ms. Kremmel was powerful in the classroom, given her authority and position to define acceptable ways of communicating mathematically. Unlike other classrooms where teachers may disregard or brush aside such language obstacles, Ms. Kremmel used her position to establish an equitable learning environment for all students. Third, Ms. Kremmel was addressing her students' social competencies through her behavior; that is, students were expected to respectfully engage with Oksana and take time to understand her thinking. Last,

Ms. Kremmel was illustrating to her students—English learners included—that they would not be allowed to sit silently in mathematics class, for she knew that such positioning of students was unfair, inequitable, and reduced their opportunities to learn (Pappamihiel 2002). This and other similar classroom events are evidence of Ms. Kremmel's commitment to developing her students' mathematics, language, and social competencies.

Drawing on Oksana's Family as a Resource

Teachers of English learners should "view parents as intellectual resources" (Civil, Planas, and Quintos 2005, p. 82), not as obstacles. Ms. Kremmel was invested in Oksana's success and conveyed this message to her family. Although Oksana's parents were Ukrainian and spoke only Russian, Ms. Kremmel did not assume that they were disengaged or uninterested in their daughter's education, beliefs that run counter to research findings (e.g., Valdés 1996). Just as Oksana used technology to translate in the classroom, Ms. Kremmel employed this technique when communicating with Oksana's family, thereby expanding the acceptance of multiple modes of communication beyond the classroom walls to bridge languages. At home, for example, as Oksana worked on her assignments, questions would arise that her family was unable to answer. In such cases, Oksana would ask her brother, who was proficient in English, to translate the family's questions from Russian to English for Ms. Kremmel. Then, Oksana would bring these questions to school. This method of communication established a relationship between Ms. Kremmel and Oksana's family and positioned language as a valuable resource. Moreover, it indicated to Oksana's family that Ms. Kremmel was invested in her student's success and wanted to actively bridge languages. It also positioned Oksana's family as partners and resources.

Reflecting and Taking Action

Ms. Kremmel was able to successfully attend to Oksana's social, communicative, and mathematical competencies while positioning her as a valuable classroom member. In this way, Ms. Kremmel was able to overcome traditional patterns of instruction for English learners in which language is placed in the foreground and mathematics slips to the background. Moreover, she did not push social competence to the side but integrated it into her regular teaching practices. This devotion to access and equity is evidenced through the varied ways that Ms. Kremmel sought success for Oksana. First and foremost, Ms. Kremmel established a classroom community in which Oksana was positioned as a valuable contributor. Next, Ms. Kremmel expanded her notion of communication and used a range of resources to facilitate Oksana's access to high-quality instruction of mathematics and language. Rather than focus on what Oksana lacked linguistically, Ms. Kremmel sought to build on Oksana's existing language resources, attending to receptive and productive language resources in her writing, speaking, reading, and listening skills (see fig. 5.1). Additionally, Ms. Kremmel did not let her own fear affect opportunities for Oksana to learn and participate in mathematics.

We close with questions and considerations for teachers as they work to support English learners in the mathematics classroom. The questions we selected were ones that Ms. Kremmel considered as she sought to provide Oksana with access to the same content and community as her peers.

- *How can I access English learners' prior language and mathematics knowledge?*
  First, we must accept that English learners are unique, not homogenous, with different backgrounds, cultures, and educational experiences. Teachers must assess students individually and not base instructional decisions on assumptions or stereotypes. Teachers can assess students through school personnel (e.g., English-learner professionals), curriculum, or educational software, to name a few resources. Teachers might also work with their English-language specialists to use existing resources such as the WIDA framework (WIDA Consortium 2011) to better understand students' language abilities (see chapter 10 to learn more ways this framework can be used as a resource). Given the range of language capabilities that students have, teachers can also expand their notion of communication to include nonverbal modes and images. In this way, teachers can shift their focus from what students lack to what students can do. (Similar advice is provided in chapter 3 regarding special education students).

- *What do my actions relay to students about who are valuable contributors in mathematics?*
  As the authority figure and role model in the classroom, a teacher has great responsibility to establish equitable classroom norms and expectations. Teachers should take time to learn about each student's cultural background and consider how that background may lead to differences in social conventions in the school and community context. In addition, teachers need to consider how they will develop students' social competence (see chapters 8 and 9).

- *How can I position my students' families as resources?*
  Different cultures may have different expectations for teachers and schools. Teachers must be aware that parents show their support and investment in their child's success in different ways. Some may contact the teacher regularly with questions, while others may defer to the teacher's authority. Regardless, teachers should consider the ways they are communicating to parents their value as a resource.

*   *How is my own fear hindering students' mathematical success?*
    If teachers allow their own fear to overshadow their responsibilities
    in the classroom (see chapter 1), equity will not be achieved. Consider
    asking yourself: Am I refusing to call on students or asking them to
    publicly share because I am scared of what they may say? If so, what
    can I do to overcome this fear that leads to inequities in my classroom?

References

Canale, Michael, and Merrill Swain. "Theoretical Bases of Communicative Approaches to Second Language Teaching and Testing." *Applied Linguistics* 1, no. 1 (1980): 1–47.

Celedón-Pattichis, Sylvia. "Rethinking Policies and Procedures for Placing English Language Learners in Mathematics." *NABE Journal of Research and Practice* 2, no. 1 (2004): 176–92.

Celedón-Pattichis, Sylvia, and Nora Ramirez. *Beyond Good Teaching: Advancing Mathematics Education for ELLs.* Reston, Va.: National Council of Teachers of Mathematics, 2012.

Chval, Kathryn, and Óscar Chávez. "Designing Math Lessons for English Language Learners." *Mathematics Teaching in the Middle School* 17, no. 5 (2012): 261–65.

Civil, Marta, Núria Planas, and Beatriz Quintos. "Immigrant Parents' Perspectives on their Children's Mathematics Education." *ZDM—The International Journal on Mathematics Education* 37, no. 2 (2005): 81–89.

Coggins, Debra, Drew Kravin, Grace Dávila Coates, and Maria Dreux Carroll. *English Language Learners in the Mathematics Classroom.* Thousand Oaks, Calif.: Corwin, 2007.

de Araujo, Zandra. "Transferring Demand: Secondary Teachers' Selection and Enactment of Mathematics Tasks for English Language Learners." PhD diss., University of Georgia, 2012.

———. "Connections between Secondary Mathematics Teachers' Beliefs and Their Selection of Tasks for English Language Learners." *Curriculum Inquiry* (online first) (2017): 1–27.

de Araujo, Zandra, Erin Smith, and Matthew Sakow. "Reflecting on the Dialogue Regarding the Mathematics Education of English Learners." *Journal for Urban Mathematics Education* 9, no. 2 (2016): 33–48.

Flores, Barbara, Patricia Tefft Cousin, and Esteban Díaz. "Transforming Deficit Myths about Language Literacy, and Culture." *Language Arts* 68, no. 5 (1991): 369–79.

Martin-Beltrán, Melinda. "Positioning Proficiency: How Students and Teachers (De)construct Language Proficiency at School." *Linguistics and Education* 21, no. 4 (2010): 257–81.

Moschkovich, Judit. "A Situated and Sociocultural Perspective on Bilingual Mathematics Learners." *Mathematical Thinking and Learning* 4, no. 2–3 (2002):189–212.

National Council of Teachers of Mathematics (NCTM). *Principles to Actions: Ensuring Mathematical Success for All.* Reston, Va.: NCTM, 2014.

Pappamihiel, N. Elani. "English as a Second Language Students and English Language Anxiety: Issues in the Mainstream Classroom." *Research in the Teaching of English* 36, no. 3 (2002): 327–55.

Pinnow, Rachel, and Kathryn Chval. "Positioning ELLs to Develop Academic, Communicative, and Social Competencies in Mathematics." In *Common Core State Standards in Mathematics for English Language Learners: Grades K–8*, edited by Marta Civil and Erin Turner, pp. 21–34. Alexandria, Va.: TESOL International Association, 2014.

Sigley, Robert, and Louise C. Wilkinson. "Ariel's Cycles of Problem Solving: An Adolescent Acquires the Mathematics Register." *Journal of Mathematical Behavior* 40 (December 2015): 75–87.

Turner, Erin, Higinio Dominguez, Luz Maldonado, and Susan Empson. "English Learners' Participation in Mathematical Discussion: Shifting Positionings and Dynamic Identities." *Journal for Research in Mathematics Education* 44, no. 1 (2013): 199–234.

Valdés, Guadalupe. Con Respeto: *Bridging the Distances between Culturally Diverse Families and Schools: An Ethnographic Portrait*. New York: Teachers College Press, 1996.

van Langenhove, Luk, and Harré, Rom. "Introducing Positioning Theory." In *Positioning Theory: Moral Contexts of Intentional Action,* edited by Rom Harré and Luk van Langenhove, pp. 14–31. Malden, Mass.: Blackwell Publishers, 1999.

WIDA Consortium. *ACCESS for ELLs: Interpretive Guide for Score Reports*. Madison: University of Wisconsin Board of Regents, 2011. https://www.wida.us/assessment/access/scorereports/access_interpretive_guide11.pdf

Wood, Marcy B. "Mathematical Micro-Identities: Moment-to-Moment Positioning and Learning in a Fourth-Grade Classroom." *Journal for Research in Mathematics Education* 44, no. 5 (2013): 775–808.

Yoon, Bogum. "Uninvited Guests: The Influence of Teachers' Roles and Pedagogies on the Positioning of English Language Learners in the Regular Classroom." *American Educational Research Journal* 45, no. 2 (2008): 495–522.

CHAPTER 6

Bilingual Academic Development in Mathematics for Emergent to Advanced Bilingual Students

Luciana C. de Oliveira, *University of Miami*

Sabrina Sembiante, *Atlantic University*

Andrés Ramirez, *Atlantic University*

This year, in her third-grade mathematics classes, Ms. Gutiérrez (a pseudonym) has focused on teaching her students the mathematical meaning of all of the keywords that they encounter in word problems. She is convinced not only that this is a useful strategy for all students but that it is especially important for her emergent to advanced bilingual (EAB) students. Her students have learned which words connected to concepts of addition (such as *and, plus, more, altogether, total, sum, add*) and subtraction (such as *take away, take from, less than, difference, minus*). She was happy to see them approaching each word problem by searching for these key words and substituting each one for its conceptual mathematical meaning. Currently, they were working on figuring out the next word problem in their set:

> Valentine's Day is less than one week away. The owner of a flower shop is trying to gather 500 flowers altogether for the upcoming holiday. She is able to get 200 flowers on one day, but only 100 more flowers on the next day. How many more flowers does the shop owner need to achieve her goal?

Ms. Gutiérrez asked one of her EAB students to read the mathematics problem aloud. "So, girls and boys, which keywords did you find, and what do they mean?" Ms. Gutiérrez asked. She received a range of answers from students, with the first responding, "Well, as we have seen in class, we know that *less than* means subtract. In the first sentence, it says 'less than,' but I just don't know what to subtract. Does that mean we're subtracting Valentine's Day from one week away?" Ms. Gutierrez paused, answering, "Well, no, sometimes the keywords aren't being used in a mathematical way." Then another student called out, "Well, what about *altogether* in the second sentence? Usually *altogether* means adding. Does this tell us that we have to add the 500 flowers?" Ms. Gutiérrez stopped and thought. "Yes, that's what *altogether* means, but what are you adding 500 flowers to? You need to think about the main question of the word problem." A third student volunteered and added, "When it says 'only 100 more flowers' in the word problem, is that telling us to add? Ms. Gutiérrez nodded her head and said, "That's right, but what are you adding 100 flowers to?" A last student chimed in, "It's also telling us to add where the question says "How many more flowers?" Mrs. Gutiérrez frowned. "Well not really," she said, "'How many more' should let you know that you have to subtract the addition of 200 and 100 flowers from 500 flowers. So, what answers did you get, boys and girls?" The students responded with numbers ranging from 0 to 800. Mrs. Gutiérrez quickly realized that her keyword approach was leading students to focus on the keywords quite literally, without relating them to the larger context of the word problems.

Making a Commitment to Access and Equity

This vignette shows the problem with using a keyword approach to analyze word problems. Although this instruction technique would seem to be straightforward and practical, it does not help students learn about the larger genre of word problems in school mathematics or uncover meaningful structures and organization of language in mathematics. In fact, strategies like the keyword approach focus on limited parts of the larger problem and impede progress for students, especially EAB students. Making a commitment to access and equity for EAB students includes going beyond such strategies and helping these students access word problems in equitable ways by addressing NCTM's Access and Equity Principle: "An excellent mathematics program requires that all students have access to a high-quality mathematics curriculum, effective teaching and learning, high expectations, and the support and resources needed to maximize their learning potential" (NCTM 2014, p. 4). Access and equity for EAB students requires language-based mathematics instruction as more than just vocabulary. The words *accessible* and *equitable* take on a different meaning from the emphasis in recent literature on modifying the language of texts to help EAB students learn better from them (e.g., Linan-Thompson and Vaughn 2007). We present a different view of *accessible* and *equitable*: providing EAB students access to the ways in which knowledge is constructed in mathematics. By moving beyond vocabulary, we provide equitable opportunities for students to access the language of word problems and "strong support that enable[s] students to be mathematically successful" (NCTM 2014, p. 4).

Word Problems as Genre

In order to address access and equity, we focus on a typical pedagogical task in mathematics classrooms: word problems. Word problems can be seen as a specific *genre* of traditional mathematical pedagogy (Gerofsky 2004), and they frequently present significant comprehension difficulties for EAB students (Martiniello 2008) that have to do with both lexical and sentence complexity (Abedi and Lord 2001). "Lexical complexity" refers to the difficulty of the vocabulary words, and "sentence complexity" to the ways that clauses are written. Yet, word problems permeate mathematics textbooks and standardized tests, and students' abilities to solve them often are seen as important measures of mathematical understanding.

In conceiving word problems as a genre, we subscribe to the notion of genres as "staged, goal-oriented social processes" (Martin and Rose 2008, p. 6). As further explained in Martin, Christie, and Rothery, "Genres are referred to as social processes because members of a culture interact with each other to achieve them: as goal-oriented because they have evolved to get things done; and as staged because it usually takes more than one step for participants to achieve their goals" (Martin, Christie, and Rothery 1994, p. 233). When we discuss the genre of word problems, we refer to different stages or steps to reach our goals. Since the origin and use of word problems is dependent upon a pedagogical relationship around mathematics, we call word problems and the teacher/ student talk they generate a pedagogical genre (Rose 2014). "Pedagogical" further specifies the social nature of genres as defined above; and in this social relationship, the teacher and the students are main actors with specified roles seeking to accomplish a purpose. The goal of this type of pedagogical genre is to relate mathematical problems to real-life situations and to apply mathematical concepts to solving the word problems.

This chapter is based on a larger study that investigates the discourse of the content areas in English and Spanish. This project, Bilingual Academic Language Development (BALD) (de Oliveira, Ramirez, and Sembiante 2015), draws on data from school textbooks at the third- through fifth-grade levels commonly used in various states to describe how academic language is constructed and used in the two languages.

For this chapter, we focus on mathematics textbooks and the word problems found within them. Our corpus consisted of 640 mathematics word problems in English and Spanish for grades 3 through 5. Our analyses revealed that schematically, word problems have three obligatory components, which we call stages. In describing the stages, the "^" mark means "is followed by":

Orientation ^ Information Sequence ^ Query

The example in figure 6.1, from the vignette, illustrates the typical stages of word problems.

Orientation	Valentine's Day is less than one week away. The owner of a flower shop is trying to gather 500 flowers altogether for the upcoming holiday.
Information sequence	She is able to get 200 flowers on one day, but only 100 more flowers onthe next day.
Query	How many more flowers does the shop owner need to achieve her goal?

Fig. 6.1. Typical stages of word problems

The Orientation stage typically establishes the situation and introduces participants and location. In the example given in figure 6.1, we know who is doing what and for which purposes. The first sentence introduces the context of the word problem: "Valentine's Day is less than one week away." The second sentence introduces a participant—"the owner"—and a situation—"is trying to gather 500 flowers altogether." These two sentences are part of the Orientation, which often includes a mathematical reference that is usually needed to answer the problem satisfactorily. The Information Sequence stage presents information needed to solve the problem. In this example, the relevant information includes "200 flowers on one day" and "100 more flowers on the next day." Finally, the Query stage contains the question or information that needs to be answered to solve the problem. The Query in the example includes a question that starts with "how many": "How many more flowers does the shop owner need to achieve her goal?"

Framework for Analyzing Word Problems: Guiding Questions, Language Demands, and Tasks for Teachers

Expanding on the work of de Oliveira (2012) by presenting the genre of word problems, we propose five questions to help teachers identify the language demands of word problems so they can then help their students work through them: (1) What task is the student asked to perform? (2) What relevant information is presented in the word problem? (3) What mathematical concepts are presented in the information? (4) What mathematical representations and procedures can students use to solve the problem, based on the information presented and the mathematical concepts identified? and (5) What additional language demands exist in this problem?

This framework is designed for teachers to analyze word problems before they are presented to students. Each question in column 1 ("Guiding Questions to Ask") in figure 6.2 helps teachers get a better sense of the structure of a word problem and its language demands. The key aspect of this work is focusing on the mathematical concepts integrated in the word problem while identifying aspects of language with which EAB students may have difficulty. Column 1 presents the questions that will guide teachers' analysis of the word problems. The "Language Demands to Identify" column (column 2) leads teachers to focus specifically on the language used in the word problems as they address each guiding question (see chapter 7 for additional strategies). The column gives examples of possible demands that teachers can attend to in addressing the guiding questions. The list is not exhaustive, however, so teachers may find other areas that will help them address the guiding questions. The "Tasks for Teachers to Perform" column (column 3) explains to teachers what it is that they are doing when they are analyzing each word problem. We next examine how teachers can analyze the language demands of a word problem by focusing on each guiding question.

Advancing Access and Equity

In this section, we analyze a word problem in English and in Spanish at the level of genre, sentence parts or clauses, and words. We show how teachers can analyze the language demands of the sample word problem by referencing each guiding question in our proposed framework. Using this framework, teachers will be able to recognize and explicitly deconstruct the genre of word problems and provide opportunities for students to gradually apply the framework themselves. We believe that this framework provides a crucial first step in advancing access and equity for all students, EAB students included. Here is the sample word problem:

Guiding Questions to Ask	Language Demands to Identify	Tasks for Teachers to Perform
1. What task is the student asked to perform?	Type of questions and their structure—for example, how many/how much	To analyze the question in the Query stage by identifying what it is asking
2. What relevant information is presented in the word problem?	Overall clause construction—the verbs and who, what, to whom	To break down the clause by finding what information is presented in the Orientation, Information sequence, and Query stages.
3. Which mathematical concepts are presented in the information?	Specific clause construction—numerical information presented in different parts of the clause	To connect the mathematical concepts needed by looking for specific numerical information presented in the clauses of each stage
4. Which mathematical representations and procedures can students use to solve the problem, based on the information presented and the mathematical concepts identified?	Question + overall clause structure + specific clause structure	To connect all previously analyzed pieces to determine a variety of mathematical representations and procedures that can be used to solve the problem
5. What additional language demands exist in this problem?	Language "chunks": nouns, verbs, prepositional phrases within clauses—not as isolated elements. Connections between clauses to determine how different parts of the word problem are connected	To identify any aspect of language that seems problematic for EAB students and is not recognized through the previous guiding questions

Fig. 6.2. A framework for analyzing word problems, adapted from de Oliveira (2012)

Marcy is making a rectangular pen to hold her rabbits. The area of the pen should be 16 square meters with side lengths that are whole numbers. What is the least amount of fencing she needs? (GO Math! Series [Grade 3 English] 2015, p. 681)

Marcy hará un corral rectangular para sus conejos. El área debe ser 16 metros cuadrados y las longitudes de los lados deben ser números naturales. ¿Cuál es la menor cantidad de material para cercos que necesita? (GO Math! Series [Grade 3 Spanish] 2015, p. 471)

Word Problem Example

The examples in English and Spanish are taken from a popular textbook series used in bilingual dual-language programs in different school districts across the United States. We call the Spanish textbooks in these bilingual programs "mirror texts" because they are direct translations of their English counterparts. The example is a classic minimum optimization problem, calling students to identify the most, least, or best solution and to attempt several alternatives through a trial-and-error procedure.

The function of a word problem, such as in the example, is to present a situation that encourages learning and allows for teaching. The language that is used in the word-problem genre supports the teaching and learning of mathematical concepts, and the sentences and language chunks in word problems are written and organized specifically for this purpose. The sentences and language chunks within the problem are also connected and share a relationship, both descriptively, in communicating the scenario depicted in the problem, and mathematically, as information is added to form the mathematics problem. The sentences and language chunks are written and organized to function in this way in both English and Spanish and are designed to accomplish the pedagogical goals of learning and teaching mathematical concepts. We have broken the English and Spanish word problems down in tables 6.1 and 6.2 so that the stages of the word-problem genre are evident in each version. By highlighting the genre, as well as the relationships between sentences and language chunks within it that work to accomplish the goal of the genre, we showcase how a vocabulary/keyword-based approach such as the one illustrated in the vignette does not attend to these crucial features. Without an understanding of the word-problem genre and how language is organized for that genre, students will not be able to attach meaning successfully to keywords or other language structures that appear in mathematics word problems. Access and comprehension of word problems can only be granted for students if teachers approach each example by first recognizing the pedagogic genre that it represents and then identifying how the language in the word problem, such as clauses and specific vocabulary, is organized to carry out that purpose. In the following section, we focus on implementing this process in order to advance equity and access.

Table 6.1. Genre stages and sample word problem in English

Genre Stages	Sample Word Problem in English
Orientation Information Sequence Query	Marcy is making a rectangular pen to hold her rabbits. The area of the pen should be 16 square meters with side lengths that are whole numbers. What is the least amount of fencing she needs?

Table 6.2. Genre stages and sample word problem in Spanish

Genre Stages	Sample Word Problem in Spanish
Orientation Information Sequence Query	Marcy hará un corral rectangular para sus conejos. El área debe ser 16 metros cuadrados y las longitudes de los lados deben ser números naturales. ¿Cuál es la menor cantidad de material para cercos que necesita?

Word-problem example: genre. The first step in presenting students with a word problem is to discuss the stages of the word-problem genre. As discussed above, the Orientation in both the English and the Spanish word problems (in tables 6.1 and 6.2) establishes a situation and introduces participants and location. In this example, we know who is doing what and for which purposes ("Marcy is making a rectangular pen to hold her rabbits"). The Orientation includes a mathematical reference ("rectangular"), which is needed to answer the problem correctly. The Information Sequence presents information needed to solve the problem. In this example, the relevant information includes "16 square meters" and "side lengths that are whole numbers." Finally, the Query, realized in this example in the form of a question, is what needs to be answered to solve the problem. In the examples in tables 6.1 and 6.2, the problem is asking for the least amount of fencing needed. As can be easily seen in the tables, the Orientation ^ Information Sequence ^ Query genre stages are the same in both English and Spanish. Even though different words and word orders may be used in English and Spanish, both languages are accomplishing the same pedagogical goal of the genre (i.e., to provide students with ways of learning and applying mathematical concepts and teachers with ways of instructing them). By looking at the word-problem pedagogical text from this top-down perspective (first from a genre perspective and then from the purpose it seeks to accomplish), a shared experience around the text and its purpose may be facilitated. Experience and knowledge encoded in the first language of the students (and their families) can be readily used in word problems and transferred to a second language in a useful way. This assets-based perspective regarding the first language was absent not only from the bottom-up keyword perspective in the vignette but also from the mathematical knowledge of EAB students and their families. Note that in the word problem shown in tables

6.1 and 6.2, the Spanish text is a direct translation from English, so the manner in which the Spanish word problem is written is quite similar to the original version written in English.

Word-problem example: guiding questions. These guiding questions are intended to help teachers analyze the word problems. We also discuss some challenges these questions may present for EAB students and how to possibly address these challenges.

- Guiding Question 1: What task is the student asked to perform?

    Once the analysis of the genre has been conducted, the first step in helping EAB students solve a word problem is for teachers to identify the specific task found in the Query stage of the problem, captured in the question being asked. Word problems often have questions, ending in question marks (?) that determine the task required by the problem. Sometimes the task is stated in the imperative mood ("Find the area of the rectangle") rather than in interrogative form ("What is the area of the rectangle?").

For example, the question in our sample word problem is "What is the least amount of fencing she needs?" The question asks for a specific type of information from students. Although the rest of the word problem discusses other technical terminology and concepts related to rectangle, area, and whole numbers, it is important that teachers clarify for students that the response needed for the question is about finding the least amount with regard to the fencing, or perimeter, of the pen for the rabbits. Several language demands embedded in the wording of the question need to be explored further. To afford students the opportunity to comprehend the question and respond correctly, teachers must guide their students to recognize the construction of the question as well as potential challenges around the language used in that question that may prohibit or confound students' understanding. These are the first necessary steps that teachers take in answering Guiding Question 1, What task is the student asked to perform?

- Guiding Question 2: What relevant information is presented in the word problem?

    To understand and respond correctly to word problems, students must note particular pieces of information in the question. Teachers can determine what information is important by identifying the type of details provided throughout the problem. The first sentence of the sample word problem (part of the Orientation stage) provides details about a human participant (the who), her actions and what the participant is acting upon (the what), and reasoning around the action (the why). When comparing these sentences across their English and Spanish versions, we see some small differences in language. Although both are written in subject-verb-object order (i.e., "Marcy" is the subject, "is making" or "hará" is the verb, and "a rectangular pen" or "un corral rectangular" is the object), there is a slight difference in the last phrase of the sentence: "to hold her rabbits" or "para sus conejos." In English, the phrase begins with the preposition "to" telling us the function of the rectangular pen, whereas in Spanish, the phrase can be translated to mean "for her rabbits" and thus identifies what the pen is for rather than its purpose of "holding" the rabbits. In both cases, the who, what, and why of the Orientation stage are effectively communicated.

The second stage of the word-problem genre, the Information Sequence stage, provides necessary details about the task to be completed. In the second sentence of the sample word problem, specific information is provided about the size of the area and the length of the sides, two pieces of information that are essential to solving the problem. Last, the Query stage asks the central question, identifying the required content and form of the answer. In the sample word problem, the answer requires students to provide the least amount of fencing: in other words, the smallest perimeter possible.

Clauses and Relevant Information Provided in the Sample Word Problem

Figure 6.3 helps teachers delineate the relevant information in each stage of a word problem. Teachers can use this figure to understand the construction of word problems and ways in which crucial mathematical information is organized in different clauses. By analyzing and identifying these aspects, teachers can help students develop the same skills so that they can locate the information needed to solve the problem. Thus, teachers can answer Guiding Question 2 ("What relevant information is presented in the word problem?") by recognizing and separating different parts of clauses by the types of information they provide and looking specifically at the different genre stages.

- Guiding Question 3: Which mathematical concepts are presented in the information?

Teachers also need to identify the mathematical concepts at work in a word problem by connecting the relevant information that they

Clause	Relevant Information Provided
Marcy is making a rectangular pen to hold her rabbits.	Who? = Marcy What is she doing? = is making What? = a rectangular pen For what purpose? = to hold her rabbits
The area of the pen should be 16 square meters with side lengths that are whole numbers.	Who/What? = the area of the pen Details/description about the pen = should be 16 square meters With what attributes? = with side lengths that are whole numbers
What is the least amount of fencing that she needs?	What? = the least amount of fencing Details/description about the fencing = needed by Marcy

Fig. 6.3. Breaking down the sample word problem into clauses and relevant information

pinpointed in Guiding Question 2 with the mathematics concepts needed to solve the problem. For example, our analysis showed that the question is asking about an amount: "what is the least amount of fencing." Having identified the relevant information, teachers can now turn to the language of the problem and the mathematical concepts that they index. Figure 6.3, based on de Oliveira (2012), can help teachers interpret mathematical concepts from relevant information in the problem.

Information Provided and Mathematizing the Problem Situation

Mathematizing the word problem's situation and linking it to the information provided in the problem is an important step, presented in table 6.3. The first step is to recognize that *pen*, as it is used in clause 1, means a fenced-in holding area, and that its shape is rectangular, meaning that it has four sides, which may or may not be equal in length. Students might confuse this specialized use of *pen* with the more everyday meaning of *pen* as a writing instrument. Clause 2 provides important information about the area of the pen (16 square meters) and specifies that the length of the sides should be whole numbers, limiting the multiples of 16 to three choices: 1×16; 2×8; 4×4. Given the relevant information from Clause 1 that specifies the pen as rectangular in shape and understanding that a rectangle is a special type of square, students should determine that all three choices of the multiples of 16 are valid. The central question of the problem is presented in Clause 3, asking for the least amount of fencing needed by Marcy, a classic minimum optimization question for third graders in geometry. Fencing for the pen would require a measurement of the pen's perimeter, and the least amount indicates the lowest number to that end. After reviewing the answers of the three choices of the multiples of 16 (34, 20, and 16), it is evident that the correct choice, totaling the least amount of fencing, would be 16 meters, the perimeter for a 4 × 4 pen. Thus, there are several pieces of information in this problem that relate to mathematical concepts (e.g., a square is a special type of rectangle; area is calculated by multiplying length and width; perimeter is calculated by adding the two lengths and two widths of a rectangle), and that require an understanding and an interpretation of the language used in the problem (e.g., *pen* to mean a type of cage; *fencing* to relate to perimeter). This task involves finding the perimeter with the given information of area. Moreover, students need to understand that rectangles are a type of square and need to be able to retrieve and apply the equation for area. Explicit connections regarding these mathematical concepts and steps need to be made for EAB students before they can start to solve the problem. Teachers can answer Guiding Question 3 ("Which mathematical concepts are presented in the information?") by identifying how the mathematics concepts connect to the language of the word problem.

Table 6.3. Relating the information provided in the sample word problem to mathematizing the situation

Information Provided	Mathematizing the Problem Situation
Clause 1: Marcy is making *a rectangular pen* to hold her rabbits.	A rectangular pen = 4 sides
Clause 2: The area of the pen should be *16 square meters* with *side lengths that are whole numbers.*	Area of pen = 16 square meters Side lengths (in whole numbers) need to be multiples of 16 Length × Width 1 × 16 (would be a rectangle) 2 × 8 (would be a rectangle) 4 × 4 (would be a square—a special type of rectangle)
Clause 3: What is the *least amount of fencing* she needs?	Fencing = perimeter Least amount = smallest number (in meters) Length (L) × Width (W) = L + W + L + W (four sides) = amount 1 × 16 = 1 + 16 + 1 + 16 = 34 2 × 8 = 2 + 8 + 2 + 8 = 20 4 × 4 = 4 + 4 + 4 + 4 = 16 Least amount = 16 meters of fencing

- Guiding Question 4. What mathematical representations and procedures can be used to solve the problem, based on the information presented and the mathematical concepts identified?

Each of the guiding questions can be used to help teachers determine a variety of mathematical representations and procedures needed to solve the word problem and to point these out to their EAB students. The first mathematical step in the procedure to demonstrate to students is identifying the equation for calculating area (area = length × width) as well as the multiples of 16 that are whole numbers. By using graphic representations of 16 square meters with different lengths and widths (see fig. 6.4), students can be guided to understand the difference in shape based on the distribution of the area. The next procedure requires identifying the equation for calculating the perimeter of an area. Multiples of 16 (representing length and width) are placed in the equation to calculate the rectangle's perimeter: length + width + length + width, or in the case of the multiple of 2 × 8,

$$2 + 8 + 2 + 8,$$

equaling a perimeter of 20 meters. Subsequently, students should calculate the perimeter of the other multiples of 16, including 1 × 16 (totaling 34) and 4 × 4 (totaling 16), keeping in mind that 4 × 4 qualifies as a rectangle as discussed under Guiding Question 3. In comparing the totals of the equations for perimeter of the three multiples of 16 (1 × 16; 2 × 8; 4 × 4), it is evident that the solution to the question of the least amount of fencing she needs is 16 feet. Figure 6.4 shows how to merge the information in the problem, the underlying mathematical concepts, and the mathematical representations and procedures to solve the problem.

Information Provided, Mathematical Concepts, and Mathematical Representations and Procedures in the Sample Word Problem

Figure 6.4 helps teachers extract the underlying mathematics concepts from mathematics language for EAB students and provide them with a procedure for understanding the mathematics-word-problem genre and how to access the solution. Following step-by-step through the preceding guiding questions can help teachers answer Guiding Question 4, What mathematical representations and procedures can be used to solve the problem, based on the information presented and the mathematical concepts identified?

Information Provided	Mathematical Concepts	Mathematical Representations and Procedures
Clause 1: Marcy is making a <u>rectangular pen</u> to hold her rabbits.	A rectangular pen = 4 sides	Length × Width 1×16 (a rectangle) 16 1 ▭▭▭▭▭▭▭▭▭▭▭▭▭▭▭▭ 2×8 (a rectangle) 8 2 ▭▭▭▭▭▭▭▭
Clause 2: The area of the pen should be <u>16 square meters</u> with <u>side lengths that are whole numbers</u>.	Area of pen = 16 square meters Side lengths (in whole numbers) = need to be multiples of 16	4×4 (a square—a special type of rectangle) 4 4 ▦
Clause 3: What is the <u>least amount of fencing</u> she needs?	Fencing = perimeter Least amount = smallest number (in meters)	Length (L) × Width (W) = L + W + L + W (four sides) = amount $1 \times 16 = 1 + 16 + 1 + 16 = 34$ 16 1 ▭▭▭▭▭▭▭▭▭▭▭▭▭▭▭▭ $2 \times 8 = 2 + 8 + 2 + 8 = 20$ 8 2 ▭▭▭▭▭▭▭▭ $4 \times 4 = 4 + 4 + 4 + 4 = 16$ 4 4 ▦ Least amount = 16 meters of fencing

Fig. 6.4. Connections among the information provided, the mathematical concepts, and the mathematical representations and procedures in the sample word problem

• Guiding Question 5. What additional language demands exist in this problem?

In addition to technical mathematics language, there are other language "chunks" that can be challenging for EAB students if not identified and discussed directly. These include clauses that offer a combination of noun, verb, and prepositional phrases, which can be unclear or difficult to comprehend. Instead of isolating language structures in world problem, teachers are encouraged to help students learn about the function of each part of the word problem and the information it contains. One example of a challenging language feature in word problems is reference devices, which are words that make a connection back to a previous source of information or which replace another word (Schleppegrell and de Oliveira 2006). In the sample word problem (see tables 6.1 and 6.2), "she" in clause 3 is a reference back to Marcy in clause 1. The noun group "a rectangular pen" in clause 1 is referenced as "the pen" in clause 2. Teachers also need to attend to homonyms, or words that are spelled and pronounced alike but have different meanings. *Pen,* in clause 1, could easily be misinterpreted by students as a writing instrument instead of as a cage for animals. Another example of language demands is the use of the nontechnical word *fencing* to signify the perimeter of the area, showcasing how crucial it is for students to understand general vocabulary as well as academic vocabulary. Students have to conjure the image of a fence in order to connect to the mathematical version of the idea as represented by perimeter. Similarly, when reading the question in clause 3, they have to identify that the wording "least amount" means "smallest number"; and since the question does not specify which unit of fencing, students will have to make the connection that the least amount relates to meters rather than meters squared. All of these aspects can encumber students and obstruct them from understanding and solving the word problem, which is why Guiding Question 5 ("What additional language demands exist in this problem?") helps teachers consider these additional linguistic aspects.

The examination around the language of this word problem, as presented through the guiding questions, demonstrates ways that teachers can gain insight into the construction of word problems and their mathematical meaning. This framework can be used to help make mathematics word problems accessible to English language learners by giving them entry into the ways in which knowledge is encoded in mathematics word problems. Rather than rewrite and simplify math word problems for EAB students, the goal should be to increase teachers' understanding and ability to instruct students on the genres of mathematical disciplinary discourse.

We have focused our approach for access and equity on the organization and structure of mathematics word problems in both English and Spanish because this encourages teachers to work beyond vocabulary and keywords, which do not help EAB students understand the larger genre and discourse of mathematics (chapters 5 and 10 also take a similar position). We showcased a sample third-grade word problem to demonstrate the steps that teachers can take in helping students understand the content and language of word problems. We also engaged in a contrastive analysis of the language and mathematical concepts in an English and Spanish word problem. We shift the dialogue from exclusive focus on language demands of academic texts for bilinguals to language affordances exclusively available to bilinguals in dealing with language demands. We contend that approaching a pedagogic genre such as the word problem as a unit of meaning first and then proceeding with a detailed analysis of clauses and specific vocabulary will enhance comprehension and access for all students and, therefore, make access and equity key components of this approach.

Reflecting and Taking Action

1. Why are word problems particularly challenging for EAB students?

2. Consider the issues presented in the vignette. How could this framework have addressed these issues?

3. Are there other genres in mathematics teaching that you can identify? Why are they important in mathematics teaching and learning?

4. In what ways does initially analyzing the genre and its purpose encourage cross-linguistic connections for EAB students and validate their and their families' first languages as useful for schoolwork?

5. Why are access and equity a key issue for EAB students and their teachers, as described in this chapter? What other access and equity issues can you identify for EAB students in mathematics?

6. How can teachers be better prepared to address the needs of EAB students in mathematics classrooms, beyond addressing their linguistic needs?

Reflect on the ways in which mathematics instruction draws on the discourse of mathematics. Identify what could be challenging for EAB students, and plan instruction to address those challenges. Consider what these students bring to the classroom as resources, and draw on their existing expertise in two or more languages. Discuss with your colleagues ways in which word problems can be taken apart for *all* students so that they can have better access to the ways in which mathematics is constructed. Work with colleagues to consider other access and equity issues for EAB students in your school and beyond.

References

Abedi, Jamal, and Carol Lord. "The Language Factor in Mathematics Tests." *Applied Measurement in Education* 14, no. 3 (2001): 219–34.

de Oliveira, Luciana C. "The Language Demands of Word Problems for English Language Learners." In *Beyond Good Teaching: Advancing Mathematics Education for ELLs*, edited by Sylvia Celedón-Pattichis and Nora Ramirez, pp. 195–205. Reston, Va.: National Council of Teachers of Mathematics, 2012.

de Oliveira, Luciana C., Andrés Ramirez, and Sabrina Sembiante. "Project BALD: Bilingual Academic Language Development." Unpublished summary. 2015

Gerofsky, Susan. *A Man Left Albuquerque Heading East: Word Problems as Genre in Mathematics Education*. New York: Peter Lang, 2004.

GO Math! Series, Grade 3 English and Spanish. Boston: Houghton Mifflin, 2015.

Linan-Thompson, Sylvia, and Sharon Vaughn. *Research-Based Methods of Reading Instruction for English Language Learners, Grades K–4*. Alexandria, Va.: Association for Supervision and Curriculum Development, 2007.

Martin, James R., Frances Christie, and Joan Rothery. "Social Process in Education: A Reply to Sawyer and Watson (and Others)." In *Language, Literacy and Learning in Educational Practice*, edited by Janet Maybin and Barry Stierer, pp. 58–82. Clevedon, England: Multilingual Matters, 1994.

Martin, James R., and David Rose. *Genre Relations: Mapping Culture*. Oakville, Conn: Equinox Publishing, 2008.

Martiniello, Maria. "Language and the Performance of English-Language Learners in Math Word Problems." *Harvard Educational Review* 78, no. 2 (Summer 2008): 333–68.

National Council of Teachers of Mathematics (NCTM). *Principles to Actions Executive Summary*. Reston, Va.: National Council of Teachers of Mathematics, 2014. https://www.nctm.org/uploadedFiles/Standards_and_Positions/PtAExecutiveSummary.pdf

Rose, David. "Analysing Pedagogic Discourse: An Approach from Genre and Register." *Functional Linguistics* 1, no.1 (2014): 1–32. doi:10.1186/s40554-014-0011-4

Schleppegrell, Mary J., and Luciana C. de Oliveira. "An Integrated Language and Content Approach for History Teachers." *Journal of English for Academic Purposes* 5, no. 4 (2006): 254–68.

CHAPTER 7

Meaningful Mathematical Discussions That Matter

Kathleen Jablon Stoehr, *Santa Clara University*

Puja Patel, *Landmark Elementary School, Glendale, Arizona*

Ms. Patel taught third grade at a K–grade 8 school of approximately 650 students. In the school, 95 percent of students were from Latino/a backgrounds; almost all qualified for free or reduced lunch. Ms. Patel's students were mainly emerging bilinguals who spoke Spanish at home and were learning English in school. The linguistic language policy of the school required that all whole-group instruction be in English. Ms. Patel adhered to these policies in her mathematics instruction. As an Indian American, Ms. Patel had begun school speaking only Gujarati (a language spoken in the state of Gujarat in India), a situation that she recalls as particularly challenging. Her own background as an English language learner informed her commitment to provide her students with an equitable educational experience.

In addition, Ms. Patel participated in a teacher preparation program and early career research project called Teachers Empowered to Advance Change in Mathematics (Teach MATH). The overarching goal of the study was "to transform preK-8 mathematics teacher preparation so that teachers are equipped with powerful strategies to increase mathematics learning in our nation's increasingly diverse public schools" (Turner et al. 2012, p. 68). Ms. Patel first participated in the Teach MATH project during her mathematics methods course and student teaching, and she then continued through the end of her third year as a practicing teacher. Sample activities during her early career teaching included ongoing study groups, monthly phone calls or emails, regular classroom observations, and pre-observation and debrief interviews. The following vignette occurred during one of the classroom observations conducted as part of the Teach MATH project.

The mathematics lesson for the day begins with Ms. Patel asking her third-grade students to help her solve mathematics problems. She asks them what they know about cats. After students provide different attributes about cats (furry, have a tail, meow, have whiskers), one student shares that they have four legs. Ms. Patel then tells them that one of the tasks for the day is figuring out how many total legs different quantities of cats have and writing a number sentence that explains their thinking. Starting with how many legs three cats have in all, Ms. Patel asks that her students work with a partner to solve this problem in at least two ways (including a picture) and be ready to share their thinking with the class. She reviews the possible strategies they might consider (repeated addition, skip counting, counting up, etc.).

While Ms. Patel walks around the classroom listening to her students' mathematical conversations, she discovers that although many of her students have concluded that the answer is twelve, some pairs of students have drawn three cats with four legs while other pairs of students have drawn four cats with three legs. She begins a conversation with two of her students who have drawn four cats with three legs.

Ms. Patel: Tell me about your drawing.

Student: I have four cats with three legs each.

Ms. Patel: What is your number sentence?

Student: Four times three equals twelve.

Ms. Patel: So how many legs does each of your cats have?

Student: Three.

Ms. Patel: So how many legs do you have in all?

Student: Twelve.

Ms. Patel: Do either of you have a cat?

Student: No, but my neighbor has a cat.

Ms. Patel: How many legs does your neighbor's cat have?

Student: Four.

Ms. Patel: Can you think about what your drawing says and then we can discuss it again.

Students: Yes.

[*Ms. Patel moves to another pair across the room.*]

Ms. Patel: Can you tell me about your thinking?

Student: I drew three cats with four legs so that equals twelve legs in all.

Ms. Patel: Tell me about your number sentence.

Student: Three times four equals twelve.

Ms. Patel: [*talking to the student's partner*]: Can you tell me about your thinking?

Student: I drew three cats with four legs. My number sentence is three times four equals twelve.

Ms. Patel scans the room and sees that her students are done with the first problem. She invites her students to bring their work and join her on the rug. She asks for a volunteer to share his or her work with the class. A student raises her hand, and Ms. Patel has her display her work on the document camera to share it with the class.

Student: I drew three cats with four legs. Then I added 4 + 4 + 4 together to get twelve. Then I knew 3 × 4 = 12. So there are twelve legs on three cats.

Ms. Patel asks the class if everyone agrees with what is written on the document camera and asks them to talk it over with their partners. After giving her class time to discuss the answer and reasoning on the document camera, Ms. Patel asks her class if twelve is the correct answer. All students agree.

To address the different equations that students produced to represent this problem, Ms. Patel writes 3 + 3 + 3 + 3 = 12 on the document camera and asks her students to discuss with their partner if this is the same problem as 4 + 4 + 4 = 12. After thirty seconds of discussion, the students agree that the problems are the same because the answer is twelve for both. With input from her students, Ms. Patel draws the picture of what the second equation means (4 cats with 3 legs each). She asks the class if the two problems are the same (4 × 3 = 12 and 3 × 4 = 12). Most of the class thinks the two equations are the same.

Ms. Patel then has the class divide into two groups: one group who believes the two number sentences mean the same thing because the answer to both is twelve and the other group who thinks the number sentences are different. Thirteen students think that the word problem can be represented by 4×3, and six students believe that it cannot. As this rich mathematical discussion continues, some students switch to the side that believes that 3×4 is not the same equation as 4×3. There is great discussion as the students wrestle with this problem. For example, the students who believe that the two number sentences are the same hold steadfast to thinking that because the answer is twelve for both number sentences, the number sentences are the same. The students who believe that the two number sentences are different draw the attention of the class to the pictures of the three-legged cats and the four-legged cats. They explain that the pictures reveal the difference. The mathematics lesson ends with Ms. Patel telling her class that they will continue to discuss these two number sentences the next day. Ms. Patel comments how these types of rich mathematical conversation help her students work toward gaining the understanding they need in order to be successful with this concept.

Making a Commitment to Access and Equity

Ms. Patel's commitment to "beliefs and practices that empower all students to participate meaningfully in learning mathematics" (NCTM 2014, p. 60), as well as her belief that "all students are capable of making sense of and persevering in solving challenging mathematics problems and should be expected to do so" (NCTM 2014, p. 64), guides her mathematics teaching (see chapter 1). Returning to the cats-and-legs problem, Ms. Patel engages her students in mathematical discussions where all students are valued for their strategies and thinking. She particularly aims to showcase students who are less confident in mathematics and whose classmates do not see them as mathematically competent.

Thinking again about the cats and legs problem, when Ms. Patel asked the class if it was correct to say three cats with four legs could be written as either $4 \times 3 = 12$ or $3 \times 4 = 12$, most of the class said both were correct, given that the answer was twelve in both cases. However, one of the students, Jorge, was brave enough to stand up and say he disagreed because they were two different number sentences. The students who disagreed with Jorge and his few followers argued that the number sentences were the same because the answer was the same. This conversation continued for several minutes before Ms. Patel helped guide Jorge into using his picture to explain his thinking. Eventually, Jorge was able to articulate that $3 \times 4 = 12$ means there are 3 cats with 4 legs and that $4 \times 3 = 12$ means there are 4 cats with 3 legs. Jorge and his fellow thinkers slowly convinced more students. Part of Ms. Patel's classroom norms are that when students are engaged in a mathematical conversation, they need to explain their thinking and make it visible to their classmates. This effort helps make their learning more meaningful, and in cases where there is disagreement and debate about the mathematics, it demonstrates sense making and builds perseverance. Moreover, Ms. Patel sends the message to her students that she expects 100 percent engagement in creating mathematical meaning, as all student voices need to be heard.

Although the most students in Ms. Patel's class were English language learners, some students were more confident than others when speaking or presenting their work to the class. Jorge was an English language learner who was less comfortable talking in front of his peers (see chapter 5). In addition, the students who were more vocal and disagreed with Jorge's mathematical reasoning were seen as the more mathematically successful students in the classroom. This persuaded many of the other students to agree that Jorge's explanation could not be right because the "smarter" students did not think so. As much as Ms. Patel worked to showcase that all of her students were capable in this content area, her students tended to be more persuaded by some of their classmates than by others. Because the students had matriculated through the lower elementary grades in the same school, their beliefs about who was better than others at mathematics were deep-seated. However, when Jorge was able to successfully show that $4 \times 3 = 12$ was not the same problem as $3 \times 4 = 12$, their beliefs began to change.

After the rich discussion that day, Jorge's status among his peers rose. Ms. Patel viewed this as a stepping-stone in her students' understanding that mathematical competency does not belong to a select few. In other words, all students are capable of making mathematical sense and have knowledge to share (Featherstone et al. 2011). Mathematical discussions like the one about cats and their legs occurred in Ms. Patel's classroom on a regular basis, creating a space for students like Jorge to build their confidence in sharing their mathematical thinking while also learning English. Moreover, these rich mathematical conversations eventually helped students understand the importance of working together to learn mathematics instead of relying solely on the explanations of a few "chosen" classmates. Creating rich and meaningful mathematical learning opportunities is essential in supporting the development of both the English language and mathematical competency (Chval 2012; Moschkovich 2013).

Advancing Access and Equity

Ms. Patel realized early in her teaching career that the mathematics curriculum offered by her school would need to be supplemented with outside resources in order to advance access and equity in her mathematics classroom. Ms. Patel had resources to draw on to help her create such a classroom environment, having participated in the Teach MATH research study noted above during her teacher preparation program and first years of teaching. Having learned the importance of generating mathematics lessons that provide students with multiple entry points that are connected to her students' mathematical thinking and their home and community knowledge, and that include opportunities for all students to excel, Ms. Patel works to modify the required curriculum to produce this type of learning for her class. In addition, through her own experience as an English language learner, Ms. Patel's attention to the role of language in teaching and learning mathematics is keen. She knows that getting her students to "talk" to one another about their strategies and mathematical thinking is crucial to building mathematical understanding (Chval and Chavez 2011/2012).

Classroom Norms

At the beginning of each school year, Ms. Patel, with the input from her students, establishes norms to create a classroom environment that is safe, positive, and equitable for all students. Here are a few of the example norms that are posted on the classroom wall:

> We will be respectful to each other at all times.
>
> We will listen to each other. Only one person talks at a time.
>
> Everyone gets to speak.
>
> We are a team!

These norms help impress on all students how important they are as individuals and how strong they can be as a team. Time is spent talking about how each student is unique and has different strengths to offer to the group's collaborative learning.

Productive Mathematical Discussions

Ms. Patel then focuses on the following principles from Kazemi and Hintz's (2014) work to create an equitable mathematics classroom through productive mathematical discussions (see chapter 9):

> Discussions should achieve a mathematical goal, and different types of goals require planning and leading discussions differently.

> Students need to know what and how to share so their ideas are heard and useful to others.

> Teachers need to orient students to one another and the mathematical ideas so that every member of the class is involved in achieving the goal.

> Teachers must communicate that all students are sense makers and their ideas are valued. (Kazemi and Hintz 2014, p. 2).

With these principles in mind, Ms. Patel's mathematics lessons consist of whole-class discussion, partner talk, and small-group discussions. Typically, the whole-class discussions frame the beginning and end of the lesson and take place while her students sit together on the class rug. This move helps establish mathematical sense making as a community, where everyone's input is valued and supported. When she introduces the lesson, Ms. Patel has her students turn to a partner to discuss what they know about the context of the lesson and the mathematics to be explored. In this way, students who are not ready to share their thoughts with the whole group have an opportunity to think aloud with just one other classmate.

While working on the mathematics tasks (such as the cats-and-legs problem), students are talking together in small groups of three or four students, discussing what they think the task at hand is and how they plan to solve the problem. All students are expected to participate in the small-group discussion and share their problem-solving strategies. If students in the group arrive at different answers (as often happens), then each student (or group of students) debates and defends why she or he think her or his answer is correct in a manner that is respectful. Often times, Ms. Patel gently reminds her students of their classroom norms so that all voices are heard.

While Ms. Patel's students are working in their small groups, she circulates among the groups to check on their progress toward solving their mathematics task. If anyone is stuck, Ms. Patel has that student query the group first before providing her input. This tactic works to share the authority of who owns the mathematics knowledge in the classroom, moving away from the assumption that the teacher is the one who has all the answers.

After the groups have had enough time to arrive at a solution to the mathematics task, the students return to the carpet to share their work. Ms. Patel asks for members of a group to share their work with the class. She aims to have sharing from at least one group that used a unique strategy to solve the task and to assign status to students who would benefit from others in the class seeing them as capable mathematics students (Featherstone et al. 2011). The document camera is used to showcase the students' work. Relying on the norms of the classroom, students are expected to listen respectfully to their classmates as they share their work.

Talk Moves

Throughout her mathematics lessons, Ms. Patel strives to follow Kazemi and Hintz's (2014) talk moves to facilitate deeper and richer conversations to enhance her students' conceptual understanding of mathematics, shift the power structure of mathematics from herself to her students, create opportunities for all students to participate, and offer academic language support for her class of English language learners (see chapter 6 for more on academic language). These moves include having students revoice another student's mathematical explanation. For example, during a lesson on repeating patterns, a student gave the example of the wallpaper pattern in her bedroom as a repeating pattern. Ms. Patel had several students revoice the explanation that the first student provided, as she could see that many students were confused. Ms. Patel then had the student who originally offered the wallpaper example confirm that her peers had revoiced her explanation correctly.

Ms. Patel also has students repeat in their own words what other students have shared about their mathematical thinking as a way to offer more time and experience with a particular concept or explanation. Having students share their reasoning to make sense of the mathematics being taught can be quite powerful. Ms. Patel used this talk move to have her students persevere in the challenging cats-and-legs problem with the expectation that they would debate the 3×4 and 4×3 dilemma until they reached a mutual understanding.

Ms. Patel encourages her students to use mathematics vocabulary during their mathematics lessons by referring to these words as "million-dollar words." For example, Ms. Patel began a lesson on measurement by reminding her students that they had been finding the size of the outside of shapes. When a student shared that they had been finding the perimeter of shapes, Ms. Patel said, "Yes, perimeter is our million-dollar word." She had her students talk to their partners to define *perimeter*. After thirty seconds, Ms. Patel pulled her class back together and called on a girl to give a definition of perimeter, and the student shared that it is the outside of a shape. Ms. Patel finds that this talk move—drawing her students' attention to the million-dollar word (perimeter) and revoicing and defining it for the class—helps create understanding of important mathematics vocabulary.

Adding on to another student's explanation is another way in which Ms. Patel strives for meaningful mathematical participation in her classroom. Ms. Patel finds this to be a powerful and inclusive learning strategy, as one student's thinking can spur on another student's thought process. Providing adequate wait time also enhances the mathematics learning of Ms. Patel's students. She has found that students often need time to organize their thoughts before they are willing to share their ideas with others. Moreover, if she tells her students that they have, for example, one minute to think about a question, then she works hard to give them the full minute to think.

Turning and talking to a partner is a talk move that Ms. Patel finds particularly empowering in creating meaningful mathematics learning. This move can serve as a stepping-stone for students to become more comfortable with and confident about sharing their strategies with the larger group of students. Turning and talking to a partner also gives students longer exposure to the mathematics being presented. Finally, allowing students to change their thinking when presented with other students' explanations or reasoning allows for more flexibility and fluidity in problem solving. Once again, with the cats-and-legs scenario, Ms. Patel offered her students multiple opportunities to switch groups if they revised their own mathematical thinking after hearing the mathematical reasoning of their classmates. Offering students the opportunity to revise their thinking exemplifies NCTM's *Principles to Actions* (2014), which states, "all students are capable of making sense of and persevering in solving challenging mathematics problems and should be expected to do so" (NCTM 2014, p. 64).

Show Me: The Power of Visuals

Ms. Patel's teaching philosophy includes offering students visuals to support their mathematical learning, a practice that Moschkovich (2002) believes can be particularly useful for English language learners. Ms. Patel uses visual representations as a means for students to access learning instead of just telling them. For example, Ms. Patel posed a multiplication word problem about the number of days in three weeks. Several of her students thought there were five days in a week since that is how many days they come to school. Instead of just telling them that there are seven days in a week, Ms. Patel took them to the class calendar and had them count the days. With the calendar in front of them, the students were able to understand what the mathematics task was and to successfully solve the problem.

As a teacher, Ms. Patel finds that many times the linguistic demands of the activities need to be addressed in order for students to solve the mathematics. To help students explain their thinking, she uses several techniques that she learned from the work of Celedón-Pattichis and Ramirez (2012). While engaging in word problems, Ms. Patel and her students break down each word to increase students' understanding of the problem. As students work on the mathematical task, sentence starters are used to help students explain their thinking. In addition, Ms. Patel encourages her students to draw pictures that reflect their thinking.

In other instances, Ms. Patel works with her students to create understanding of new words or words they are unsure about. For example, when students were given a word problem about bouquets of flowers, a group of students did not understand what a bouquet was. Ms. Patel used her phone to show them a picture of a bouquet of flowers. Another instance occurred when a mathematics task involved figuring out how many cups of yogurt were in a specific number of yogurt packs. While students were working in their groups, Ms. Patel noticed that the members of several groups were rather quiet and had puzzled expressions on their faces. When she asked them to tell her about their thinking, one student asked, "Ms. Patel, what is a pack?" Immediately Ms. Patel brought her laptop computer to the table to show the students a picture of cups of yogurt that were packaged together. In these two cases, once the students had an image that showed what the word meant, they were able to use multiple strategies (pictures, repeated addition, etc.) to solve the problems. Ms. Patel believes that using visuals not only supports her students' academic language but also increases their conversational English. Pictures that show the meaning of a word can also create confidence in language. Sometimes when students see a picture that "defines" a word they do not initially recognize, they realize that they know what the item actually is but had not yet made the formal connection between the item and the word. In this way, a picture can serve as a bridge to language.

Ms. Patel shares an example of a group of students who were struggling to solve a challenging division problem about sharing an equal number of items among a given number of people. The students were not able to connect with the example given in the problem, so Ms. Patel changed the task to sharing rubber-band bracelets (an item that her students were currently interested in) and sharing them among the students in their table group. The students' goal now was to share with the people at their table instead of sharing that involved an abstract concept. This alteration in the problem helped the group visualize what they were doing, and by using a manipulative (cubes) to represent each bracelet, they were able to successfully solve the problem. By scaffolding her students' learning, Ms. Patel gave them the message that she expected them to be able to do the mathematics.

Through visual representations, Ms. Patel's students also see that they do not need to rely on her to do the mathematical thinking. By "showing" her students what an unfamiliar word means, the students are the ones still solving and thinking through the mathematics problems. When Ms. Patel offers the necessary language support, her students are more likely to make sense of the mathematics and persevere to solve rigorous mathematics tasks.

Ms. Patel's experience in teaching English language learners has taught her the importance of getting to know her students' language needs so that they can feel more confident in engaging in their mathematics learning. Students who are English language learners may be hesitant to speak, let alone share their mathematical thinking. Therefore, creating classroom practices that empower students in mathematics is critical. Ms. Patel finds that some students are able to understand mathematics in an abstract fashion, some need to draw pictures, and others need manipulatives in front of them in order to access the mathematics. However, all students need to understand the language of mathematics in order to be successful. Language support for all students in the mathematics classroom is essential.

Smartness for All

Ms. Patel is committed to creating a classroom environment in which all students are seen as having mathematics smartness. As Featherstone and colleagues (2011) point out, students who believe that they are capable mathematics students are more apt to engage in productive struggles when presented with challenging mathematics tasks. Therefore, Ms. Patel believes that she must showcase the different types of smartness that her students possess so that students see themselves as smart—and their peers see them as smart, too.

By having students work in small groups, Ms. Patel is able to move around her classroom, listen to her students' thinking as they work on a mathematical task, and make note of which student or small group she would like to have present answers at the close of the lesson. Returning to the cats-and-legs problem, Jorge was a student who was seen as having low status in the classroom. While most of the class disagreed with Jorge's reasoning that 4×3 was not the same as 3×4, it created a perfect opportunity for Ms. Patel to "assign competence" to Jorge in front of his classmates. As Featherstone and colleagues's (2011) work reveals, teachers are in a powerful position to assign competence "(1) to help high-status students appreciate the intellectual contributions of lower-status classmates, (2) to help low-status students appreciate their own 'math smarts,' and (3) to call attention to useful strategies that one or more students have devised in working on a problem" (p. 87). This is how Ms. Patel's classroom norms, her productive classroom discussions, talk moves, and visuals come together as a means to support every student to develop mathematical competence over time. "Smart is not an all-or-nothing attribute" (Featherstone et al. 2011, p. 20). Rather, Ms. Patel believes that all students, when given the appropriate support, are "math smart." (See also chapter 9.)

Table 7.1. Summary of Ms. Patel's strategies to support access and equity in her mathematics classroom

Norms	Principles of Productive Mathematics Discussions (Kazemi and Hintz 2014)	Talk Moves (Kazemi and Hintz 2014)	Visuals (Celedón-Pattichis and Ramírez 2012)	Status (Featherstone et al. 2011)
We will be respectful at all times.	Discussions should achieve a mathematical goal, and different types of goals require planning and leading discussions differently.	Revoicing	Representing words through pictures (e.g., pictures of cups of yogurt, packs of yogurt, bouquet of flowers)	Help high-status students appreciate the intellectual contributions of lower-status classmates.
We will listen to each other.	Students need to know what and how to share so their ideas are heard and useful to one another.	Repeating	Sentence Starters (e.g., There are . . . The balls cost . . . . He bought . . .)	Help low-status students appreciate their own "math smarts."
Only one person talks at a time.	Teachers need to orient students to one another and the mathematical ideas so that every member of the class is involved in achieving the goal.	Adding on	Manipulatives	Call attention to useful strategies that one or more students have devised in working on a problem.
Everyone gets to speak.	Teachers must communicate that all students are sense makers and their ideas are valued.	Wait time	Adjust the task so students can "see" it or relate to it.	
We are a team!		Turn and talk		
		Revise		

Reflecting and Taking Action

As Ms. Patel reflects on her first four years of teaching, she thinks about how learning to teach in general is a work in progress, let alone learning to teach mathematics in an equitable manner. However, she believes that the two cannot be separated. Instead, they need to be learned hand-in-hand so that all the students entrusted in her care can learn in an equitable manner. Table 7.1 summarizes the strategies discussed in this chapter that Ms. Patel uses in her classroom to support access and equity for all her students.

Ms. Patel shares the following key points as she thinks about the lessons she has learned while striving to be a teacher who works to advance the mathematical learning of all her students:

- Know that it is OK for students to get incorrect answers. As tempting as it is to "show" students where they made their mistakes and fix the mistakes for them, work toward having students construct their own meaning.

- When working in pairs or groups, guidelines and expectations must be clear so that students stay on task. Different types of thinkers should be a part of each group.

* Teach students to use respectful words when working together. For example, when students do not agree on an answer or strategy, saying "I do not understand your thinking" (instead of "I think you are wrong") is a positive way to keep the group moving forward.

- Help students build stamina so that they will push themselves to do the mathematics and persevere.

- Provide guiding questions when setting up mathematics tasks.

- Have students write their answers in complete sentences so that they can identify what the answer means.

- Drawing pictures is a powerful way for students to "see" their thinking.

- Trust that your students are intelligent and are capable of learning the mathematics.

- Provide individual opportunities for all students to experience success and publicly showcase their success to their peers.

- Remember that we have all been faced with learning new mathematical concepts. Provide ample learning time so that students can think it through. Experiencing mathematics is much more valuable than just being shown mathematics.

In closing, we present a few questions for teachers to consider as they think about and commit to an equitable and accessible mathematics classroom for all students:

- Are the students and the teacher attending to the established classroom norms?

- Who is doing the talking?

- Are students working alone, in pairs, or in small groups?

- Do daily productive mathematical discussions take place?

- Is the language in the mathematical tasks accessible to all my students?

- What status issues do I need to attend to among my students?

- Is my classroom a "safe place" for students to share their thinking?

- Is the mathematics being taught in my classroom connected to my students' daily experiences?

- Are the mathematical tasks open-ended with multiple entry points and strategies?

- Are there visuals to support student learning?

- Are mistakes encouraged?

Acknowledgments

This material is based on work supported by the National Science Foundation under Grants No. 1020155 and No. 0736964. Any opinions, findings, and conclusions or recommendations expressed in this material are those of the authors and do not necessarily reflect the views of the National Science Foundation.

References

Celedón-Pattichis, Sylvia, and Nora Ramirez. *Beyond Good Teaching: Advancing Mathematics Education for ELLs*. Reston, Va.: National Council of Teachers of Mathematics, 2012.

Chval, Kathryn. "Facilitating the Participation of Latino English Language Learners: Learning from an Effective Teacher." In *Beyond Good Teaching: Advancing Mathematics Education for ELLs*, edited by Sylvia Celedón-Pattichis and Nora G. Ramirez, pp. 77–88. Reston, Va.: National Council of Teachers of Mathematics, 2012.

Chval, Kathryn B., and Oscar Chavez. "Designing Math Lessons for English Language Learners." *Mathematics Teaching in the Middle School* 17 (December 2011/January 2012): 261–65.

Featherstone, Heather, Sandra Crespo, Lisa Jilk, Joy Oslund, Amy Parks, and Marcy Wood. *Smarter Together: Collaboration and Equity in the Elementary Math Classroom*. Reston, Va.: National Council of Teachers of Mathematics, 2011.

Kazemi, Elham, and Allison Hintz. *Intentional Talk: How to Structure and Lead Productive Mathematical Discussions*. Portland, Maine: Stenhouse Publishers, 2014.

Moschkovich, Judit N. "A Situated and Sociocultural Perspective on Bilingual Mathematics Learners." *Mathematical Thinking and Learning* 4, no. 2–3 (2002): 189–212.

———. "Principles and Guidelines for Equitable Mathematics Teaching Practices and Materials for English Language Learners." *Journal of Urban Mathematics Education*, 6, no. 6 (2013): 45–57.

National Council of Teachers of Mathematics (NCTM). *Principles to Actions: Ensuring Mathematical Success for All*. Reston, Va.: NCTM, 2014.

Turner, Erin, Corey Drake, Amy Roth McDuffie, Julia Aguirre, Tanya Gau Bartell, and Mary Foote. "Promoting Equity in Mathematics Teacher Preparation: A Framework for Advancing Teacher Learning of Children's Multiple Mathematics Knowledge Bases." *Journal of Mathematics Teacher Education* 15, no. 1 (2012): 67–82.

CHAPTER 8

Promoting Equity, Access, and Success through Productive Student Partnerships

Kathryn B. Chval, Rachel J. Pinnow, Erin Smith,
and Oscar Rojas Perez, *University of Missouri*

Linda (all names are pseudonyms), a third-grade teacher, works in a school with a student population that is primarily white. In recent years, Latina/o emergent bilingual children receiving ESL services have begun to attend Linda's school. Linda began her third year of teaching with three Latina/o students: Mariano, Santiago, and Daniela. She admitted that her teacher preparation program had not prepared her to teach emergent bilingual learners, especially in the context of teaching mathematics. Linda's typical mathematics lessons involved an introduction to the lesson on the carpet, student pairs working together to solve mathematics problems, and then a debrief session with the whole class on the carpet.

As Linda circulated the classroom to observe student partnerships, she began to question her decision-making practices related to selecting student partners. At the beginning of the school year, she did not have sufficient information about the children's social, communicative, and mathematical competencies to make informed decisions about productive partnerships. Linda wanted to create a classroom culture in which any two students could be successful and productive partners. She often used random selection by choosing, out of a cup, pairs of Popsicle sticks with the students' names written on them. As Linda began to observe student partnerships involving Mariano, Santiago, and Daniela, she noticed some student behavior that concerned her a great deal. She saw partners dominate interactions with the Latina/o children. For example, a girl grabbed Daniela's pencil out of her hand to complete her work for her. John positioned their handouts in front of him so that Santiago was the spectator. Mariano, Santiago, and Daniela had limited opportunities to speak in their partnerships because their partners dominated the conversation. In some cases, body language and tone of voice communicated that the partners of Mariano, Santiago, and Daniela did not value their contributions and did not perceive them as competent. For example, they ignored their questions, suggestions, and requests, and on occasion were disrespectful or just downright mean. With the guidance of a researcher, Linda began to reflect on a series of questions about partnerships, including:

- What are qualities of productive and unproductive partnerships for children in mathematics classrooms?

- What are factors that influence productive and unproductive partnerships in mathematics classrooms?

- What criteria do you consider when selecting partnerships for emergent bilingual learners?

- How do you facilitate productive partnerships for emergent bilingual learners?

- How do you handle situations involving unproductive partnerships with emergent bilingual learners?

Over the course of three years, a research team video recorded Linda's mathematics lessons, including student partnerships involving her Latina/o learners. Linda met with the lead researcher over the course of twelve weeks each year to view videos of these partnerships so that she could improve her practice. In this chapter, we introduce strategies and resources that Linda (and a few other teachers) used in our research projects, as well as challenges that they encountered as they began to examine this aspect of their practice.

Making a Commitment to Access and Equity

The preceding vignette illustrates challenges that many students face on a daily basis as they negotiate peer interactions during mathematics lessons. However, it also illustrates Linda's commitment to access and equity as she invested time to learn how to facilitate productive partnerships for all her students, especially her Latina/o emergent bilingual learners. *Principles to Actions: Ensuring Mathematical Success for All* (National Council of Teachers of Mathematics [NCTM] 2014) emphasizes productive beliefs about equity and access, including these:

- All students are capable of participating and achieving in mathematics, and all deserve support to achieve at the highest levels.

- Students who are not fluent in English can learn the language of mathematics at grade level or beyond at the same time that they are learning English when appropriate instructional strategies are used.

- Effective mathematics instruction leverages students' culture, conditions, and language to support and enhance mathematics learning.

- The practice of isolating low-achieving students in low-level or slower-paced mathematics groups should be eliminated. (pp. 63–64)

In addition to productive beliefs, *Principles to Actions* (NCTM 2014) also emphasizes the importance of classroom community on student participation and engagement:

> Classroom environments that foster a sense of community that allows students to express their mathematical ideas—together with norms that expect students to communicate their mathematical thinking to their peers and teacher, both orally and in writing, using the language of mathematics—positively affect participation and engagement among all students (Horn 2012; Webel 2010). (p. 66)

Achieving the Access and Equity Principle requires productive beliefs and practices on the part of students and teachers. Teachers serve as models. If teachers position some children differentially, then students' behavior will mirror that positioning (Yoon 2008). In excerpt 1, for example, consider how John, a fourth-grade teacher with whom we worked, positions Rob, a monolingual English speaker, and Janessa, a Latina emergent bilingual, at the beginning of their partnership. (Note that during this lesson all the other children in the classroom selected their own partners; however, John made the decision to pair Janessa with Rob.)

Excerpt 1: You're Going to Go Janessa's Speed

1	*John:*	Now Janessa, Rob's gonna work with you today, okay?
2	*Janessa:*	Thank you.
3	*Rob:*	[*looks at his paper and taps his pencil against his paper*]
4	*John:*	So that means you work the same speed, Rob. What do you think, how could
5		you explain this first one to her?

6		[*John returns a little later to check on Rob and Janessa.*]
7	*John:*	Now go a little slower. [*looks at Rob*] Work with the second one [*pulls Janessa's*
8		*paper closer to Rob's*], okay? I'm going to walk around a little. You're [*referring to*
9		*Rob*] going to go Janessa's speed today, okay?

Excerpt 1 illustrates an obstacle to the vision outlined in *Principles to Actions*: The teacher positioned Rob as the mathematical expert who needs to help Janessa. NCTM (2014) argues that teachers may believe that some students can "do math" while others cannot. Janessa's teacher made this partnering decision based on his beliefs about what Janessa could not do, which limited her participation and success in this partnership. This is evidenced by the way John frames the pace of the problem solving as "a little slower" (line 7), one that works at "Janessa's speed" (line 9).

Other common misconceptions about students can hinder teachers from creating classroom environments that promote academic success for all learners. For instance, it is a common misconception that emergent bilingual learners should not be taught grade-level mathematics until they are proficient in English; but in reality, these students can and should be taught mathematics as they are learning the English language in order to develop linguistically, academically, and cognitively (Chval, Pinnow, and Thomas 2015; Gibbons 2015; NCTM 2014). Since students learn through interacting with the language of specific content areas (Schleppegrell 2004), it is critical that all learners experience productive partnerships where their ideas are attended to and they have the time necessary to work out mathematical meanings (NCTM 2014). Therefore, it is important to understand factors that create an environment where all students understand how to engage in and value productive partnerships. Moreover, bilingual education researchers argue that the development of English proficiency requires students to use English in active and dialogic communication that is purposeful, such as working to understand one another's meanings during discussion or while solving problems (Mohan and Slater 2005).

Excerpt 2 offers an example of an inequitable pairing that Eduardo, a Latino emergent bilingual learner, experienced in Courtney's third-grade mathematics class. In the excerpt, Eduardo has been paired with Stefan, a native English speaker, to complete a mathematics problem that required the use of Unifix cubes. This example highlights what emergent bilingual children may encounter in partner work when teachers are not present.

Excerpt 2: Copycatter

1	*Eduardo:*	It starts with green black green black green black green black green black . . .
2	*Stefan:*	[*interrupts and talks over Eduardo*] I'm starting with like . . .
3 4	*Eduardo:*	[*interrupts Stefan*] We're starting wi–with this one. [*picks up and rotates Unifix cube stick*]
5 6 7	*Courtney:*	So I see that Stefan was labeling, so Eduardo, maybe you could take a turn doing something next time? [*stands and watches for a moment and then moves to another group*]
8	*Stefan:*	[*gestures on ticker tape*] So, this one's green, that one's black.
9 10	*Eduardo:*	This one's black, this one is green, that's green, black, green. [*picks up Unifix cube stick and holds it upright, perpendicular to desk*]
11	*Stefan:*	Put it down.
12	*Eduardo:*	Green black green black.
13	*Stefan:*	Dude, you're going to start from the four. So either green black or black green.
14	*Eduardo:*	Black green.
15 16	*Stefan:*	So you're going to start on this side. Black green black green black green, on this side. So start with black.
17	*Eduardo:*	I know. [*speaks quietly and colors the cube with a pencil on his paper*]
18	*Stefan:*	I'm going to go from your side. Color the whole black thing.
19	*Eduardo:*	I know. [*whiny high-pitched tone*]
20	*Stefan:*	No you don't. [*whiny high-pitched* tone]
21	*Eduardo:*	Oh, no?
22	*Stefan:*	Copycatter. [*reaches over and marks off the task on Eduardo's paper*]
23	*Eduardo:*	[*sits silently coloring*]

This excerpt shows the type of unproductive partnerships Eduardo routinely experienced early in the school year, where his peer interrupts and talks over him (excerpt 2, line 2), dominates the necessary materials (line 11), dominates the discussion (lines 11, 13, and 18), corrects Eduardo's ideas (line 20), and engages in name calling (line 22). Because group work has become central to the learning process in mathematics classrooms, teachers must ensure that emergent bilingual learners are equipped for success in these situations. Before we share strategies implemented by some teachers in grades 3–5, we suggest you reflect on the situations in figure 8.1 (next page) and consider how you would respond to each situation.

Advancing Access and Equity

Teachers play a key role in partnering students so that emergent bilingual learners have regular opportunities to share their ideas and are then positioned in the classroom environment as competent community members (Yoon 2008). The teachers with whom we have worked over the years have identified a number

Imagine you encountered each of these six situations with different pairs of students, one an emergent bilingual student and one a native English speaker.

• The two students are working independently and not collaborating.

• The emergent bilingual student appears to be completely disengaged.

• One student has used an algorithm (that has not yet been taught) and is explaining it to his or her partner. However, the partner is unfamiliar with the algorithm and is struggling to understand the procedure.

• The native English speaker is completing all the work for both students while the emergent bilingual student watches.

• The native English speaker grabs the pencil from the emergent bilingual student and begins writing on the emergent bilingual student's paper.

• The native English speaker is continually dismissing the emergent bilingual's thinking and strategies.

Fig. 8.1. Partnering situations

of characteristics for productive partnerships, which are listed in the left-hand column of table 8.1. In addition, Cobb (1995) recommends that classroom teachers establish norms in mathematics classrooms that facilitate high-quality partnerships. These norms are listed in the right-hand column of table 8.1. Of course, accomplishing these characteristics and norms consistently across different student groupings is complex and challenging, and it requires significant investment of time to establish, maintain, and promote.

In this section, we use examples from Courtney, a third-grade teacher, and Sara, a fifth-grade teacher, whose practices we have researched (see for example, Chval 2012 and Chval, Pinnow and Thomas 2015), as well as research to illustrate teaching practices that have facilitated equitable partnerships for emergent bilingual learners in mathematics classrooms. We organize these ideas into four subsections describing how teachers can (*a*) establish an environment in which students respect one another and value partnerships, (*b*) use criteria for partner

Table 8.1. Characteristics of productive partnerships and classroom norms that facilitate them

Characteristics of productive partnerships	Norms that support productive partnerships
Communicate and listen effectively	Perseverance required to solve challenging problems
Value other people and their ideas and strategies	Explanation of one's solutions to a partner
Learn from and challenge one another.	Listening to partner explanations and attempting to make sense of those explanations
Contribute to solving the assigned mathematical tasks and challenges	Challenge of partner explanations that seem unreasonable
Use time effectively	Justifications when challenged by a partner
Share the floor with others so there is an equitable distribution of roles	Attempts to reach an agreement on a solution or solution method

selection, (*c*) identify subtle cues that indicate inequitable partnership patterns, and (*d*) use strategies to intervene when necessary.

Establish an Environment in Which Students Respect One Another and Value Partnerships

One important strategy teachers can draw on is to identify what makes for productive partnerships and plan a conversation with all students about participation norms in the classroom. Although the teacher initiates this conversation, it should draw on ideas from students, since students are more likely to adhere to norms that they themselves generate (e.g., listening and not interrupting when others speak, not speaking over peers when they are talking, respectfully disagreeing with the ideas of others, encouraging peers to participate, and making appropriate eye contact). This type of conversation is important because it generates specific practices that benefit emergent bilingual learners, as suggested by NCTM (2014) (e.g., additional wait time to process questions and compose verbal answers, inclusion of all learners rather than privileging particular groups). It is also important because it is a means to build the capacity of native-speaking students and students who may have been historically privileged in mathematics programs to work productively and equitably with peers who may come from backgrounds different from their own (Tabors 2008).

Courtney used a strategy, which she referred to as "compliments," that promoted mutual respect among students—a basis for productive partnerships. Courtney facilitated a discussion about the use of compliments during mathematics class. She had a box in the room where students could place compliments that they would write about one another during their spare time. At the end of the day, as the students packed up and prepared to leave, Courtney read compliments that had been written by students (anonymously). Of course,

Courtney slid a few compliments into the box to ensure that all the children in her classroom received compliments.

Another approach Courtney created was the "friendly reminder" that was attached to each student desk so that the students had examples of questions and compliments to use in their partnerships (see fig. 8.2). Courtney also modeled and role-played examples of productive and unproductive partnerships, asking students how they would feel in those situations. As she observed productive aspects of partnerships, she highlighted them as examples for students to emulate in the future.

Questions:

- What did you do first?
- How can we start?
- What do you think?
- How did you solve that problem?
- Would drawing a picture help?
- How can I help you?
- How else could we solve this problem?

Compliments:

- I like your math thinking.
- I like your picture.
- Thank you for helping me.
- You did a good job.

Fig. 8.2. Friendly reminders

In addition to communicating value and interest in the ideas of others, an important part of mathematics is disagreement, argumentation, and justification. Sara, a fifth-grade teacher, recognized the importance of disagreement and argumentation in partnerships in mathematics classrooms. She created an environment in which disagreement was cooperative, positive, and valued. Sara communicated that family members who share, care, help, respect, and listen are in a position to construct viable arguments and critique the reasoning of others. She also positioned students as contributors, family members, teachers, role models, and experts. For example, Sara set up students' roles as teachers during the first week of the school year, as shown in excerpt 3.

Excerpt 3: Expecting Competency in Students and Drawing on These Competencies

Sara: So Dalia was asking Alejandro, and Alejandro didn't know what to do. Alejandro wasn't participating because he never asked for help. So somebody over here. Anybody. You move around. I'm only one person. Move around quietly and ask each other. You can teach each other. Walk around. Help each other. I can't help all of you at the same time.

As the researcher observed Sara's approach during this lesson, she noted that the students did not know how to respond (i.e., they stared at each other in disbelief). This was a new norm for them, as the typical practice in earlier grade levels did not give the students the autonomy to participate in that way. Sara later established the norm that "help," in this case, did not mean doing the work or thinking for someone else. (For a more thorough description of this aspect of Sara's practice, see Chval [2012].) Once teachers conduct conversations about how to engage in equitable discussion and debate, it can be beneficial for them to focus on patterns of partnering students. Partnering practices in the classroom should be intentional and attend to students' need for a variety of experiences.

Use Criteria for Partner Selection

When we asked teachers to identify the characteristics they would use in selecting partners of emergent bilingual learners, the following list resulted:

- Strong communicator
- Personable
- Positive use of social cues
- Relational and pleasant
- Engaging inside and outside the classroom
- Encouraging and supportive
- Patient
- Willing to yield control

It is not surprising that the teachers identified ideal characteristics that would be helpful in interacting with others. For example, the list reflects characteristics used to describe individuals in social services, such as elementary school teachers, social workers, and nurses. Almost all these characteristics focus on personality traits, with only one characteristic (i.e., strong communicator) focused on language competencies. A list like this one suggests that the emergent bilingual learner would only interact with a small percentage of elementary school children. To create the type of learner suggested by the list, teachers would need to invest time in teaching students how to participate in productive partnerships.

As Courtney began the school year, she used observation and trial and error to identify productive partners for her emergent bilingual learners. She would often find herself in situations where the trial failed. For example, she did not want native English speakers who dominated all the speaking or partners who displayed biases against different culture groups. She ultimately wanted to be able to pair her emergent bilingual learners with anyone in the classroom. However, she knew accomplishing that goal would take the bulk of the school year. Therefore, her selection criteria at the beginning of the year differed from her criteria at the end of the year. At the beginning of the year, for example, emergent bilingual learners might not yet have the tools to navigate challenging interactions, as discussed in Pinnow and Chval (2015). Courtney also recognized that at certain times it was advantageous to partner emergent bilingual learners with other emergent bilingual students, while at other times pairing emergent bilingual learners with monolingual English speakers was an appropriate strategy. Thus, over time, Courtney fashioned a teaching toolkit that provided her with both the tools she needed and the insight to draw on those tools at the appropriate time given the circumstances of different pairings.

Identify Subtle Cues That Indicate Inequitable Partnership Patterns

Teachers can learn to notice subtle cues and take them into account when observing students' partnership activities, including these:

- *Who speaks first* when the teacher joins the group?

- *Which* student speaks for the group when the teacher approaches the group or interacts with the group?

- *How* did this student become the spokesperson for the group (i.e., was this a group decision or did one student simply take on that role)?

- Are the same students the spokespeople during partnering work?

- How often are emergent bilingual students the spokespeople for their groups and how did this status evolve in the group?

Another important cue that teachers can take into consideration is *who controls the materials* that have been used for problem solving. For instance, when partners use manipulatives, where are they located on the table when the teacher joins a particular group? Are the materials regularly located in front of one particular student and not others? Do students appear to share materials, with emergent bilingual learners having access to those materials? Who uses these materials when explaining what the group did?

The teacher should also consider where students sit and how they arrange themselves physically. Avoiding odd-numbered groups can be an important strategy to avoid fostering inequities among students (e.g., there are an equal number of students in the entire class, but the teacher divides students in threes, which can foster inequities as two students join forces against the third student).

Finally, what happens when emergent bilingual learners speak or share their ideas? Do the other students listen respectfully or do they speak or make noises while emergent bilingual learners are speaking? Do other students interrupt or talk over emergent bilingual students so that they have difficulty completing their ideas aloud? What do patterns of disagreement look like in these partnerships? Do all students know how to disagree without being disagreeable? For instance, once an emergent bilingual learner has shared his or her ideas, do other students consider the idea and respectfully question or disagree, or does the interaction begin to devolve into unproductive interactions?

Use Strategies to Intervene When Necessary

As Eduardo's teacher, Courtney, became aware of the unproductive results of the partnerships Eduardo experienced in her classroom (see excerpt 2), she began to apply strategies to counter these inequities. Courtney began to approach partnering from the perspective that students need to discuss their mathematical problem-solving strategies in order to learn mathematics and to develop the mathematical language required to explain those concepts to others. This approach also addressed the need to teach students to persevere in problem solving and to explain their ideas to others. Courtney began to note instances where she could position Eduardo in ways that privileged his ideas and created a platform for him to contribute to his partnerships. Since his partners did not always listen to him and, at times, imposed ideas on him, Courtney made specific moves to open up discussions to include Eduardo.

Courtney's approach did not mean that Eduardo did not experience turbulence in interactions with his peers. However, her actions positioned Eduardo differently within these possibly challenging partnerships so that he had opportunities to be the leader of the interaction, rather than positioned as someone who always needed the "help" of others (Pinnow and Chval 2014), and he was able to successfully defend his ideas so that others recognized the accuracy of his mathematical thinking. Courtney's strategies can be identified in excerpt 4. In this excerpt, Courtney paired Eduardo with Betsy to complete a mathematical task. Eduardo's work, along with the problem, are shown in figure 8.3.

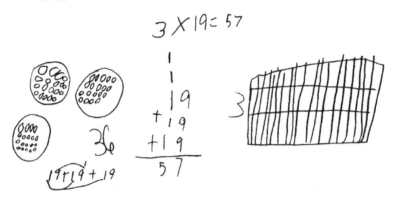

1. There are 3 baskets of puppies. There are 19 puppies in each basket. How many puppies were there in all? 5 7

Fig. 8.3. Eduardo's work for the puppy problem

Betsy was considered a dominant personality in Courtney's classroom. Pairing her with Eduardo was intentional so that Eduardo had practice navigating diverse types of interactions. Initially, Betsy dominates both the mathematics conversation and the mathematics materials. However, Courtney carefully reorients this situation when she joins the pair.

Excerpt 4: I Already Knew That

1	Betsy:	Can I see this? [*takes Eduardo's worksheet and writes on it without his consent*]
2	Eduardo:	[*looks at Betsy and then around the room*]
3 4 5	Betsy:	This is what I did. I put this together and then this together and then all this together, okay. [*writes answers on Eduardo's paper*] Fourteen plus nine, so I put two down here and a seven up there.
6	Eduardo:	[*looks at his paper, which Betsy is holding, and shakes his head*] Mm-mm, no.
7	Betsy:	Nine. [*speaks over Eduardo and continues to work*]
8 9	Eduardo:	[*points with the eraser of his pencil to a spot on the paper that Betsy holds*] Like, there's three right there and here.
10	Betsy:	[*stops writing*]
11 12	Eduardo:	[*points with the eraser of his pencil again*] Like, three and you add these, and that's twenty-seven. You put the twenty together . . . goes to fifty . . .

13	Betsy:	How'd you get fifty-seven? [*starts checking Eduardo's work by counting out*
14		*the boxes on the paper aloud*]
15	Eduardo:	[*listens as Betsy counts aloud*] You're gonna see it's fifty-seven.
16	Betsy:	[*keeps counting aloud*] Thirty-six . . . I got thirty-six . . .
17	Courtney:	[*sits down with Eduardo and Betsy at the table*]
18	Betsy:	[*looks at Courtney*] I, like, I picked the biggest number and that's what I went with.
19	Courtney:	Oh, okay.
20	Betsy:	So it's really not . . . five blocks. How many did . . . we have in them? Okay.
21	Courtney:	Okay, Eduardo, can we look at this one together? Eduardo, you've got a
22		couple different things that you've got going on.
23	Eduardo:	Uh, this one is Betsy's 'cause she, she thought it was a hundred and two and I . . .
24		[*looks at Courtney*]
25	Courtney:	And you think it's fifty-seven? [*points and smiles at Eduardo as she speaks to him*]
26	Eduardo:	Yeah.
27	Courtney:	Okay, so are you trying to help her out with this?
28	Eduardo:	[*nods his head*]
29	Courtney:	Okay, so what do you . . . how would you explain this so far? Have you
30		explained it to Betsy yet?
31	Eduardo:	[*shakes head "no"*]
32	Courtney:	Okay, so you explain there what you have done and then she explains what
33		she has done and then we'll figure out what it is.
34	Eduardo:	I chose, I chose nineteen.
35	Betsy:	[*begins to mutter under her breath as Eduardo speaks*]
36	Eduardo:	Three rolls and then nineteen . . . Fifty-seven because I counted all of them.
37	Courtney:	And then what's that picture you have with those circles? What's that?
38	Eduardo:	Puppies [*laughs*] puppies in a basket.
39	Courtney:	Okay so that's the picture of the puppies? [*points at the picture*]
40	Eduardo:	[*nods head*]
41	Courtney:	So, okay, can you bring your paper over here so she can look at what you did?
42	Eduardo:	[*moves the paper over for Betsy to see*]
43	Courtney:	Okay, so you see here? He did an array where he did three groups of nineteen
44		puppies and he counted every one and found fifty-seven and then here. Did
45		you get fifty-seven, too?
46	Betsy:	[*states something that is unclear*]

[Lines 47–57: Courtney walks through the mathematics problem with Betsy while Eduardo listens.]

58	Courtney:	Okay, so Eduardo, what do you think Betsy did here?
59	Eduardo:	Umm [*clears throat*], I think that this one that she did, she forget to put the
60		number here [*points to the paper with his pencil*] so she got twenty-seven.
61	Courtney:	Yeah.
62	Eduardo:	I already knew that.
63	Courtney:	You already knew that. [*smiles at Eduardo*]

    In excerpt 4, challenges arise that are similar to those in excerpt 2 as
Eduardo's partner, Betsy, dominates the materials necessary to complete the task

(line 1), even writing on Eduardo's paper for him (line 4), although her answers are incorrect (line 6). She also refuses to acknowledge Eduardo's ideas, instead treating Eduardo's work as potentially inaccurate (lines 13–16). Betsy speaks the most in the interaction and initiates the conversation with Courtney when Courtney sits down at the table (line 17). This is an important and subtle cue for teachers to notice, since dominant students often present themselves to the teacher as the primary problem solver and representative of the partnership.

Courtney responds to Betsy's initiation (line 19) but includes Eduardo so that he can share his mathematical thinking (lines 21–22). This is an important action on Courtney's part as it creates a platform for Eduardo to be an active member in problem solving, sharing mathematical strategies, and navigating possible mathematical errors and how they occurred. Initially, Courtney clarifies whose work is on the paper (lines 21–22). Eduardo notes that the incorrect work is Betsy's (lines 23–24). Courtney then positions Betsy as one who needs Eduardo's "help" (line 27). This is an important role reversal for Eduardo: His mathematical answer is the correct one, and he can assist others in effective problem solving. When Courtney asks Eduardo if he has explained the answer to Betsy, he indicates that he has not (lines 29–30), and Courtney makes space for each partner to explain his or her problem solving (lines 32–33). Something interesting occurs at this point in the interaction. As Eduardo begins to explain his answer (line 34), Betsy begins to mutter under her breath, in effect still attempting to speak over Eduardo (line 35). Eduardo keeps speaking, explaining his mathematical solution (line 36).

Because of Betsy's muttering under her breath, Courtney takes over the explanation, drawing out Betsy's problem solving to find where the strategy may have gone awry (lines 43–45, 47–57). Courtney then asks Eduardo to weigh in on what might have gone wrong (line 58), and he explains his perspective (lines 59–60), which Courtney ratifies (lines 61 and 63).

Reflecting and Taking Action

The excerpts above demonstrate the obstacles that emergent bilingual learners and teachers can experience in mathematics classrooms and the strategies that can be implemented to encourage equitable participation through productive partnerships. Emergent bilingual learners do not need every interaction to be smooth, with no challenges. This would be impossible to achieve, since students will experience challenging interactions throughout their lives. Instead, preparing students to navigate such interactions is a critical skill for future success. In addition, all students benefit from learning how to be a productive partner, a competency that is critical for gaining important communication skills when sharing mathematical ideas and problem-solving strategies and for fostering perseverance in problem solving. Since academic discussions involve a variety of perspectives, some of which students may not agree with, the expectation of being an effective communicator and partner must be instilled as part of the process of solving mathematical problems and tasks. It is worth noting that an equitable classroom environment benefits not only bilingual learners but also more dominant students (e.g., Betsy) who will require consistent messages and possibly other interventions from the teacher that the ideas of others are worthwhile and deserve respectful attention.

Reflection Questions

As the vignette at the beginning of this chapter demonstrates, effective teaching of mathematics requires attention to a variety of factors. When working with emergent bilingual students, these factors include attention to the social, communicative, and academic competencies of learners, including how students are partnered during mathematical problem-solving. One of the most important components of working effectively with emergent bilinguals is the teacher's belief that these students are capable learners. Without a mindset that recognizes the competencies that these students bring to bear on classroom learning opportunities, other strategies will not be as effective since they are framed from a deficit perspective. Instead, both teachers and students benefit tremendously from a classroom environment in which all learners are viewed as capable, competent, and eager to share their thinking. In this vein, partnering students intentionally, teaching all learners how to be a good partner, and positioning emergent bilingual learners intentionally and effectively is crucial to creating a classroom climate that fosters the rigorous thinking and the participation required for an equitable and effective mathematics learning environment.

The teachers we worked with began to ask hard questions, such as these:

- **How do I establish an environment in which students respect one another and value partnerships?** The teachers recognized that they had to work with the class to establish shared values and participation norms that include how one gains the conversational floor, how one shares the floor, and the value of listening and not talking over others so that everyone can engage in mathematical discussions necessary for mathematical thinking and learning. (See chapter 7 for discussions about classroom norms for collaborative learning.)

- **What criteria should I use when selecting partnerships for emergent bilingual learners and how does this change over the course of the school year?** The teachers recognized that they had to be aware of their students' personalities and temperaments. They had to focus on teaching more dominant students to share the problem-solving floor so that quieter students had the opportunity to contribute. They also had to make a deliberate space for emergent bilingual learners to participate, using strategies such as the ones demonstrated by Courtney in excerpt 4.

- **What are subtle cues that indicate inequitable partnership patterns?** The teachers knew they had to be observant. When they approached a small group, they had to determine which student was the first to speak and which student acted as the group representative. When they observed the groups from a distance, they took note of which student appeared to do the most talking and determined whether everyone in the group had access to the learning tools necessary for the work.

- **What strategies should I use to handle situations involving unproductive partnerships with emergent bilingual learners?** Teachers recognized that they would encounter challenging interactions, such as those demonstrated in excerpt 4, and that these challenges are actually necessary for all learners to gain competencies in mathematical discussion and debate. Rather than simply separating students or avoiding particular pairings, intervention in the midst of problematic pairings can provide a platform for students to share their ideas and frustrations, as well as for the teacher to interrupt negative positioning and provide constructive avenues to keep students on track. (See chapter 9 for more strategies that support productive collaborative work.)

It is important to remember that Courtney and Linda participated in professional development on a weekly basis over a three-year period to learn how to teach mathematics to emergent bilingual learners (see Chval and Chávez 2011/2012; Chval, Pinnow, and Thomas 2015; Estapa, Pinnow, and Chval, 2016; Pinnow and Chval 2014; and Pinnow and Chval 2015 for more information about this professional development). As they interacted with the research team, the teachers tried new strategies, enhanced curriculum materials, analyzed their practice through the use of videos, and examined the impact on their students. The teachers acknowledged that they had to invest time to learn how to support emergent bilingual learners, especially in their partnerships.

Action Plan

Work with a colleague to examine partnerships in your classroom involving emergent bilingual students. Use the reflection questions above, the partnering situations in figure 8.1, and the strategies discussed in this chapter to begin a discussion and develop an action plan. As you engage in this action plan and think through lessons with a focus on emergent bilingual learners as well as NCTM's Access and Equity Principle (NCTM 2014, p. 5), you will enhance your teaching practice, and you will also contribute to emergent bilingual learners' academic, communicative, and social success in mathematics classrooms.

Acknowledgments

This material is based on work supported by the National Science Foundation under Grant Number DRL-0844556. Any opinions, findings, conclusions, or recommendations expressed in this material are those of the authors and do not necessarily reflect the views of the National Science Foundation.

References

Chval, Kathryn B. "Facilitating the Participation of Latino English Language Learners: Learning from an Effective Teacher." In *Beyond Good Teaching: Advancing Mathematics Education for ELLs*, edited by Sylvia Celedón-Pattichis and Nora G. Ramirez, pp. 77–90, Reston, Va.: National Council of Teachers of Mathematics, 2012.

Chval, Kathryn B., and Óscar Chávez. "Designing Math Lessons for English Language Learners." *Mathematics Teaching in the Middle School* 17, no. 5 (2011/2012): 261–65.

Chval, Kathryn B., Rachel J. Pinnow, and Amanda Thomas. "Learning How to Focus on Language While Teaching Mathematics to English Language Learners: A Case Study of Courtney." *Mathematics Education Research Journal* 27, no. 1 (2015): 103–27.

Cobb, Paul. "Mathematical Learning and Small-Group Interaction: Four Case Studies." In *The Emergence of Mathematical Meaning: Interaction in Classroom Cultures*, edited by Paul Cobb and Heinrich Bauersfeld, pp. 25–129. Hillsdale, N.J.: Lawrence Erlbaum, 1995.

Estapa, Anne, Rachel J. Pinnow, and Kathryn B. Chval. "Video as a Professional Development Tool to Support Novice Teachers as They Learn to Teach English Language Learners." *The New Educator* 12, no. 1 (2016): 85–104.

Gibbons, Pauline. *Scaffolding Language, Scaffolding Learning: Teaching English Language Learners in the Mainstream Classroom.* 2nd ed. Portsmouth, N.H.: Heinemann, 2015.

Horn, Ilana. *Strength in Numbers: Collaborative Learning in Secondary Mathematics.* Reston, Va.: National Council of Teachers of Mathematics, 2012.

Mohan, Bernard, and Tammy Slater. "A Functional Perspective on the Critical 'Theory/Practice' Relation in Teaching Language and Science." *Linguistics and Education* 16, no. 2 (2005): 151–72.

National Council of Teachers of Mathematics (NCTM). *Principles to Actions: Ensuring Mathematical Success for All.* Reston, Va.: Reston, Va.: NCTM, 2014.

Pinnow, Rachel J., and Kathryn B. Chval. "Positioning ELLs to Develop Academic, Communicative, and Social Competencies in Mathematics." In *Common Core State Standards in Mathematics for English Language Learners: Grades K–8*, edited by Marta Civil and Erin Turner, pp. 21–33. Reston, Va.: National Council of Teachers of Mathematics, 2014.

———. "How Much You Wanna Bet?: Examining the Role of Positioning in the Development of L2 Learner Interactional Competencies in the Content Classroom." *Linguistics and Education* 30, (2015): 1–11.

Schleppegrell, Mary J. *The Language of Schooling: A Functional Linguistics Perspective.* Mahwah, N.J.: Lawrence Erlbaum, 2004.

Tabors, Patton O. *One Child, Two Languages: A Guide for Early Childhood Educators of Children Learning English as a Second Language.* 2nd ed. Baltimore, Md.: Paul H. Brookes Publishing, 2008.

Webel, Corey. "Shifting Mathematical Authority from Teacher to Community." *Mathematics Teacher* 104, no. 4 (2010): 315–18.

Yoon, Bogum. "Uninvited Guests: The Influence of Teachers' Roles and Pedagogies on the Positioning of English Language Learners in the Regular Classroom." *American Educational Research Journal* 45, no. 2 (2008): 495–522.

CHAPTER 9

The Problem of Overparticipation

Fostering Productive Participation in Your Classroom

Marcy B. Wood, *University of Arizona*

Maggie Hackett, *Tucson Unified School District, Arizona*

Two third-grade Latino/a students, Javier and Dominica, were working on the following problem:

> There are two baskets, a brown one and a red one, holding a total of ten eggs. The brown basket has two fewer eggs in it than the red basket. How many eggs are in each basket?

The two students sat on the carpet, with their classmates watching and listening to their problem-solving process.

Javier was Latino, outgoing with adults, and popular with his peers. He participated in many sports teams and was perceived by his teachers, peers, and himself as a good student, particularly in mathematics. Dominica, who was also Latina/o, was more reserved, especially in whole-group settings. She responded when directly asked, but in a quiet voice, which one had to strain to hear. Dominica also participated in a few sports teams and had a small circle of friends. She was usually labeled as a struggling mathematics student; and because of this and other academic weaknesses, her teachers were considering recommending her for pull-out intervention services.

After introducing the task, the teacher asked the two students to work on the problem in front of the class, explicitly directing them to say aloud what they were thinking and encouraging them to write on the whiteboard. The class was to listen to their classmates' process, think about whether they agreed with their thinking, and note what they might have done differently. The two students spent a couple minutes getting started: reading the problem, looking at each other, and checking in with the teacher for guidance.

Eventually, Javier began, "I think the answer is eight, because it says two fewer, and since we have ten eggs to start, ten minus two is eight." The teacher replied, "Okay. Dominica, what do you think about Javier's idea?" Dominica gave a noncommittal shrug and looked at Javier. This spurred Javier on, "Wait, I can show it another way!" On the board, he wrote $10 - 2 = 8$, as he repeated what he stated earlier. "So, as you can see by the math, by my equation, it's correct."

Dominica nodded her head in agreement, as did many of the other students. The teacher asked Dominica to read aloud the question in the task and then asked Javier what his answer would be, since the question was asking for how many eggs were in each basket. Javier stopped and thought for a moment, looked at the equation he wrote on the board, and then declared that eight eggs would go in one basket and ten eggs in the other. A few heads nodded in agreement from the class. The teacher asked, "But if there are ten eggs in one basket and eight eggs in the other, together that would be eighteen, and it said we only had ten eggs." She let that thought linger for a minute. The students looked at the equation written on the board, and one student said, "Well, then it would be eight eggs and two eggs, because ten minus two is eight. Javier got the right answer the first time."

The teacher asked Javier how he knew to subtract, and he replied, "Because it said fewer and fewer means to subtract." Javier's claim was met by enthusiastic head nodding from the other students. At this, the teacher asked Javier to draw his solution on the board. Javier drew a circle, labeled it "red," and put eight dots in it. He then drew a second circle, labeled it "brown," and put two dots in it. The teacher allowed a few moments for the class, along with Javier and Dominica, to study the representation, and then she asked Dominica to read the problem again.

As Dominica read, Javier was pointing at each circle and whispering, "two, eight, ten," under his breath. Dominica looked back and forth from the picture to the problem and back to the picture. The students remained silent. Finally, the teacher intervened, "I think something is wrong. This says that the brown basket has two fewer eggs than the red basket. Here, the brown basket has six fewer because eight minus two is six." The teacher then turned to the class, "What ideas do you have about what I just said?"

Making a Commitment to Access and Equity

If we look at this moment through the lens of the National Council of Teachers of Mathematics's (NCTM) Access and Equity Principle (2014), we see much to celebrate: The students have access to high-quality mathematics curriculum through the challenging mathematical question posed by the teacher. The teacher held the students to high expectations, pushing them to keep examining Javier's solution. Several students were engaged and paying attention to Javier's presentations. Javier used mathematical notation and words to communicate his ideas. Finally, the students seemed to be working toward a mathematically appropriate solution.

In spite of these causes for celebration, there is a troubling undercurrent. The Access and Equity Principle insists that *all* students have support to "maximize their learning potential" (NCTM 2014, p. 59). However, in this classroom moment, Javier seemed to be the student with the best opportunities to learn. In spite of the teacher's multiple invitations to question Javier's solution, the other students seemed reluctant to offer critiques or additional solutions; and although Dominica was invited to contribute to the conversation, she said little beyond rereading the problem. Finally, many students remained silent and mostly invisible to their peers and even to the teacher. As a result, little was known about what they understand or what mathematics, if any, they might have learned in this moment. This teacher had done so much to encourage her students to talk together and discuss mathematical ideas. Yet, the students allowed their thinking to be dominated by just one student, narrowing their opportunities to learn mathematics to Javier's way of solving this problem.

Scenarios such as the one in the vignette occur frequently in mathematics classrooms. A few students tend to dominate the discussion, contributing most of the ideas. As teachers work hard to manage the complex space and time of the mathematics classroom, it can be easy, even necessary, to allow these few students to talk so much and the other students to participate so little. However, these differences in participation result in differences in mathematical learning. These differences are even more problematic when we realize that the silent students are frequently from the most marginalized groups of students: girls, students of color, students who are learning English, and students whose families have limited financial resources. As we think about providing access and equity for students, we often focus on the level of districts, schools, or classrooms, advocating for curriculum and resources that affect groups of students. However, we must also think at the level of individual students, focusing especially on the experiences of students who are not eagerly engaged in mathematics lessons.

Involving these silent students is challenging work that requires a teacher to do more than invite their reticent voices into the conversation. Instead, the teacher must overcome deeply held beliefs about whose voices should fill the classroom space. These beliefs are not just in the heads and hearts of the silent students. They are also held by the other students and by those outside of the classroom, including parents, other teachers, administrators, and politicians.

These beliefs echo across our society. We constantly seek out "the best and the brightest," frequently identifying these people based upon their skin color, accent, gender, and wealth rather than on their specific competencies. We then set those individuals on pedestals, placing them in positions of superiority. These best and brightest then become the people whose voices and ideas are considered most valuable and most worth hearing, even when they are talking about areas outside their expertise. For example, we allow entertainment celebrities to tell us how we should vote and allow politicians without any teaching experiences to tell us how to run schools and classrooms. The point here is not that these well-known people should be silenced, but rather that those in a position of privilege too often are allowed to do all the talking. This is especially problematic in our classrooms, where the participation of each student is central to learning for all students. When some students are assumed to be the best and the brightest and to deserve more opportunities to participate, we diminish the opportunities for every student to learn, especially students who are not from privileged groups.

In this chapter, we seek to show how inequity in mathematics education is an outcome of societal messages and expectations about whose voices matter. We first explore how we make decisions about who should participate, and then we consider the consequences of those decisions. We end with several questions that teachers might ask themselves in order to start work on problems of participation in their classrooms.

Advancing Access and Equity

NCTM's Access and Equity Principle (2014) acknowledges that students arrive in our classrooms with different mathematical skills, backgrounds, and interests and cautions us that these differences do not reflect innate abilities. This caution is warranted because we have a tendency to turn even small differences in students into a fairly permanent assessment and to rank students by ability. For example, we might assume Javier was better at mathematics than Dominica. He was generating mathematical solutions and offering evidence for his reasoning while she did little more than reread the problem and nod. This comparison and ranking of Javier and Dominica becomes problematic if, in the future, we continue to assume that Javier is stronger at mathematics and start to craft mathematical opportunities that push Javier forward while leaving Dominica silent and behind.

We use the term status to describe these ideas about differences in students' mathematical abilities. Cohen and Lotan (2014) define status as a person's ranking relative to others based on perceptions of competence in a particular context. In our vignette, Javier was assumed to be better than Dominica at math. He was confident in his responses, and none of the students was willing to question his ideas. Thus Javier's status, or ranking, in mathematics was higher than Dominica's. In contrast, Dominica had fairly low status as her teachers (and probably her peers and even Dominica herself) felt that her academic skills, compared to those of other students, were relatively weak.

Status rankings can be problematic for many reasons. The ranking tends to be broadly applied so that once a student is seen as good at one thing, she or he is assumed to be academically strong in many areas. We know students who are quite good readers and who are then also assumed to be good at writing stories, understanding social studies, and solving mathematics problems. We can also see this in the scheduling of honors classes in middle school and high school. Often, if a student is seen as an honors student in one academic area, that student is scheduled for all available honors classes in the different content areas. Likewise, a student who is on the regular track or remedial track may be limited to regular or remedial track classes even if this student shows considerable skill and interest in mathematics.

Status rankings of students are also problematic because they are often based on limited and irrelevant information. High-status students, like Javier, are usually respected because they respond quickly with correct answers. While mental calculation is a valuable tool, it is not the only important mathematical skill for succeeding in school mathematics. It is the equivalent of being a tall basketball player: Everyone notices you and makes assumptions about how your height translates to basketball talent. But mathematics draws on many other skills, such as spatial reasoning and proportional thinking, that are as valuable, if not more so, than quick computation.

Status rankings may also be based on attributes unrelated to the skill being assessed. For example, many people use gender, skin color, accent, English language skills, and even clothes as part of their decision about a person's competence. These attributes are used to judge competence across a wide array of areas, including business, banking, science, acting, software design, politics, health, law, and many others. In our society, the people who are expected to be better are usually middle or upper class, men or boys, white, and with a midwestern American accent. Decisions about status are frequently made unconsciously, so we may not even notice that we mentally assign a lower status to someone, for example, whose clothes do not match our own or who struggles to ask a question in English.

As you read this description of status, perhaps you thought about how status plays out in your classroom. Our schools are a reflection of our society, and so status plays a significant role in who is seen as more capable and worthy of learning and whose rights to learn should take precedence over others. We all have students who are perceived by almost everyone as the "smartest." These students get more floor time, may be enrolled in gifted classes with teachers who have been trained to help them advance, may receive more specific feedback, and are assumed to know more. In contrast, their peers are assumed to know less, resulting in less floor time, fewer opportunities to present their ideas, and less access to challenging curricula. These differences play out at the level of districts and schools, but they also occur within our own classrooms as we and our students inadvertently provide our higher status students with more opportunities to learn. And, as we noted earlier, the label of "smart," high-status student is not based on true measures of competence. Instead our high-status students frequently reflect the gender, skin color, wealth, accent, and home language of the privileged members of our society. In this way, these status differences in our classrooms perpetuate the inequities of the larger society.

Status differences in our classrooms undermine the learning of every student. While our higher status students have more opportunities to learn, these opportunities are less robust than they would be if we could reduce or eliminate status. Higher status students often have problematic and narrow understandings of mathematics, but other students will go along with their understandings, believing that they must be correct. As with Javier's ideas in the vignette, these problematic mathematical ideas go unchallenged by lower status students, a situation that requires the teacher to intervene. Many students are willing to turn their mathematical thinking over to high-status students. Others may have questions about a solution but are unwilling to risk challenging the high-status student, feeling that their responses will be ignored or that their voices are not worth being heard. As a result, mathematical solutions go unexplored and unquestioned, limiting the mathematical learning of everyone.

Another problem with status is the value it places on certain kinds of mathematics. Our higher status students are often quite good at a limited range of activities. For example, they are frequently adept at calculations and at reading the teacher. However, they are also frequently less skilled in other mathematical areas, such as generating visual representations or clearly communicating their ideas (e.g., Lack, Swars, and Meyers 2014). These other areas are often the strengths of our low-status students, yet these strengths frequently go unnoticed because many mathematical activities rely at least partially, if not wholly, on some form of computation. Thus our high-status students can almost always find a way into a problem and can quickly declare success, while our low-status students receive little acknowledgment of their understanding of the problem.

What do we do about this situation? We must learn (and model for our students, their families, other teachers, and administrators) to notice status problems and to address them. One way to work on status is to focus specifically on student participation, considering who gets to participate and how.

Participation

Years ago, when we first began thinking about inequities in classrooms, we reflected on student status, differentiating high-status students from low-status students. However, we found that it was difficult to disconnect these status labels from other labels such as high achieving, high performing, low achieving, and knowing less. As soon as our minds linked status to performance, we easily slipped into problematic assumptions, such as that higher status students knew more and should contribute more, and we found it harder to help ourselves and others see the problems of this status differential. For example, when we talk about Javier as high status, it is sometimes easy to think about him as high ability, which then distracts us from both his mathematical weaknesses and how his participation might limit the participation of other students.

Instead, we found it useful to consider whether students were *underparticipating* or *overparticipating* and to use those labels (*underparticipator* and *overparticipator*) to help us work with participation differences. Rather than use the term low status to talk about a student like Dominica, we would note that she tended toward underparticipation, remaining mostly quiet during whole-class conversations. This participation label focuses us on the student's activities and provides us with a specific area to address. We can begin to craft opportunities to notice Dominica's mathematical strengths and then design tasks that require these strengths, allowing Dominica to find ways to successfully participate. Likewise, when our high-status students are labeled as overparticipators, we can focus on areas in which they might need to grow, such as making sense of the arguments of others, and we can redirect their participation toward those areas.

Our initial framings of overparticipation and underparticipation tended to focus on student talk, noting that overparticipators talked too much, while we heard little from the underparticipators. This framing was quite helpful as it allowed us to begin to problematize the activities of our high-status students.

We could begin to see how their talk, which we might have considered to be highly desirable, meant that others did not have opportunities to talk and that, as a group, we missed out by not hearing the many rich and varied ideas of the underparticipators.

However, limiting ourselves to student talk raised problems. That approach tended to frame participation as a zero-sum game in which there was a limited total amount of participation (i.e., talking space) that had to be carefully measured out across our students. A focus on student talk also limited our solutions to trying to balance student talk. We tried to call on the underparticipators and shush the overparticipators, but this move left the overparticipators confused and frustrated about what they were supposed to do. They knew how to talk and had been rewarded for that in the past. If they were not supposed to talk, then what were they to do? At the same time, the underparticipators were sometimes reluctant to talk, having grown accustomed to taking a back seat to overparticipators. A situation such as this is where a broader notion of participation is helpful.

If we think about participation as *taking part or sharing in* mathematical activity, we begin to see other ways that students might participate. These other forms include nonverbal communication, such as moving manipulatives, writing, graphing, and drawing. They also include taking in and reflecting on ideas through noticing, observing, listening, integrating, clarifying, and attending. Finally, taking part in mathematical activity has an important nonmathematical component: motivating, encouraging, and supporting oneself and others, especially in times where doubt and discouragement might deter students from persisting in a task.

As we think more broadly about participation, we notice other ways in which overparticipators take over mathematical activities. They do more than talk too much. They also control manipulatives, writing, and drawing. As we work with overparticipators, we want to help them limit their control over the airspace, ideas, and physical props (manipulatives and paper) and help them see how the more *relational forms of participation* (noticing, listening, and encouraging) are important aspects of mathematical learning. We can frame these relational activities as essential aspects of participation—and something at which our underparticipators are quite skilled. We can then frame underparticipators as participating in important ways (by noticing and encouraging) and note that, because of these forms of participation, they have learned things that we can all benefit from hearing about. This appreciation of the strengths of underparticipators can help them find their voices so that we can all learn more about their mathematical ideas.

As we consider the participation of our students, we need to reflect on engaging each student in multiple forms of participation across a lesson—sometimes talking, sometimes moving manipulatives, sometimes observing, sometimes reflecting, and sometimes encouraging. As we improve the kinds and qualities of participation in our classroom, we raise access to challenging and productive mathematics and improve the equity outcomes in our classrooms.

Reflecting and Taking Action

Addressing issues of status and participation is hard work, as it goes against deeply held and persistent messages about whose voice matters. One way to start this work is to recognize unproductive beliefs that reinforce the overparticipation of high-status students and the underparticipation of low-status students. We do not mean to imply that these beliefs are only held by teachers; they come from students, families, administrators, and politicians as well. We hope that by presenting and discussing them here, we can support teachers in starting to see how these beliefs have unintended negative consequences for the participation of each of their students.

1. **Unproductive belief:** *Mistakes are contagious; only correct answers and solution paths should be shared with the class.* **Productive belief:** *Students learn more by analyzing mistakes and faulty reasoning.*

As teachers, we sometimes worry that if students are exposed to a mistake or listen to a problematic explanation, they will learn and remember the wrong mathematics. As a result, we are reluctant to call on our low-status students who may hesitate or fumble with their answer. Instead we turn to our go-to students, those high-status students whose computation is usually correct and who are good at reading us and replying with the answer we want (or who can respond quickly to our hints to get to a right answer).

However, mistakes are not sticky or contagious. Instead, analyzing mistakes results in much more robust learning (Boaler 2015). Thomas Edison reminds us, "I have not failed. I've just found 10,000 ways that won't work." Students' acknowledgment and analysis of what did not work positions all students as learners. Error analysis allows the whole mathematical story to be featured, instead of skipping ahead to the punch line (the answer).

2. **Unproductive belief:** *Standardized test scores accurately reflect the appropriate level of instructional challenge for students.* **Productive belief:** *We need to challenge each of our students, identifying areas of strengths and weakness to craft lessons that push students in areas of growth.*

Assessment results frequently become tools for assigning status. We assume that the students with the highest scores are our best math students, and we accord them higher status than their lower scoring peers. We also tend to differentiate our instruction to match test scores, so our higher scoring students receive more challenging and interesting work, while the lower scoring students have "opportunities" to be retaught the material that they failed to learn the first time. We have good intentions in making these decisions. However, these decisions reinforce participation structures that allow the highest scoring students access to the most interesting ways to participate while relegating the lower scoring students to repetitive and boring participation structures that failed to be successful the first time.

Assessment scores can be useful tools in thinking about areas of student strength and weakness, but we frequently lack sufficient detail about student scores and test questions to know more than what broad content areas might not yet be well understood. Rather than rank students based upon test scores, we might see these scores as one indicator of one kind of performance. We can then use this information to design tasks that can better reveal students' understandings and areas of growth.

3. **Unproductive belief:** *Some students just do not have the confidence or disposition to participate and speak publicly.* **Productive belief:** *All students have mathematical strengths to contribute. We need to help everyone in the classroom recognize and request these strengths.*

We are sometimes reluctant to shine the spotlight on low-status students because we do not want to embarrass them. We worry that if we ask them to contribute and they falter, we will do irreparable damage to their self-image. However, when we overlook them, we also damage their self-image as we reinforce the belief that they cannot successfully participate. We can start to address this problem by helping everyone in our class see that mistakes are important opportunities to learn, as we noted earlier.

We can also identify the mathematical strengths of these students and publicly acknowledge their skills (a move we call *assigning competence*; see Featherstone et al. [2011] for more information). As we label the strengths of our low-status students, everyone in the room begins to see their mathematical competencies. These students then become experts, a label that opens doors to participation, both one-on-one as other students seek their expertise and at the whole-group level when others ask these students to respond.

4. **Unproductive belief:** *Learning is an individual endeavor that is best motivated by competition.* **Productive belief:** *Learning is a sociocultural activity in which students motivate one another to consider various perspectives.*

Cooperative learning and group work have become commonplace in classrooms across the country. And yet the belief persists that students are ultimately responsible for their own thinking and activity completion, even when working collaboratively. There also seems to be a belief that learning and knowledge are finite resources that cannot be distributed equally. In order to win at the game of school, students need to gather as much knowledge as possible, even at the expense of the knowledge available to others.

As we strive for access and equity in our classrooms, we need to significantly reduce, and even eliminate, structures that encourage competition. Competition reinforces issues of status by providing a tool that authorizes and celebrates overparticipation. Students are not encouraged to take risks and try to learn new skills. Instead, the goal for each student is to maximize participation at the expense of others. Inevitably, the overparticipators will win and the underparticipators will lose; and they lose not only the competition but also opportunities to learn new mathematics and to develop additional mathematical confidence.

5. **Unproductive belief:** *Each group needs a leader, someone who knows how to do the problem or task and can show the other students what to do.* **Productive belief:** *Each group member has something mathematical to contribute to the problem or task.*

In cooperative learning, there are often roles for students to fulfill, such as recorder, timekeeper, and resource monitor. The most coveted of roles is *captain*; and, more often than not, it goes to students who are academically strong, well organized, and can get a group task completed, with or without the help of their group mates. As teachers, we feel more secure in the accomplishments of our small groups, because we know that each group has a guiding force that can carry the group forward while we might be otherwise engaged. Even if that student does all the work, at least the group will have finished the problem, and the other students in the group might have learned a little something by watching and listening to the leader.

Unfortunately, captains quite often can be the only students who gain much learning from the cooperative learning task. While the overparticipator has an opportunity to reason through the problem and practice specific mathematical skills, the others, as passive observers, gain very little. In the same vein, the overparticipator is denied the opportunity of varying perspectives, alternate strategies, and differing viewpoints. The task might be complete, but at what cost?

These are just a few problematic beliefs that reinforce ideas about who should and should not participate. As you think about your own classroom, you might identify other beliefs that result in you and your students providing a small group of privileged students with significant opportunities to participate. The next section is designed to help you reflect on your classroom and to begin to identify what you might do to work toward equitable participation in your room.

Reflection Questions

Grappling with student participation requires reflecting on the norms and beliefs surrounding student ability and participation in your classroom. You might begin by thinking about the productive and unproductive beliefs described above. Which unproductive beliefs about participation have you found yourself using? Which unproductive beliefs are held by your students, their families, and others who enter your classroom? Which productive beliefs would you like to emphasize more? You might reflect on what motivates the unproductive beliefs you hold. Can you try embracing a more productive belief? You might also consider ways to communicate with students, families, and others about their unproductive beliefs.

Consider the forms of participation valued in your classroom. How do students typically participate? What feedback and rewards do you offer for those forms of participation? If possible, you might videotape you and your students during a few mathematics lessons. As you watch the videotape, or as you think back upon a lesson, what do you notice about the ways in which students participate? What kinds of messages do you send (intentionally or unintentionally) about the ways students should participate in your classroom?

Next, consider your students and how much they participate. Who are your overparticipators? What do they do to overparticipate, and how do they convince others that their overparticipation is justified? Who are your underparticipators? Are they disengaged? Are they working to be well behaved rather than mathematically active? Your video or earlier reflection will help you answer these questions. Pay careful attention to how students react to one another's participation. Are overparticipators reinforcing problematic participation structures by doing things such as taking manipulatives from one another or ignoring one person's ideas? What are some forms of participation that you might like overparticipators to work on? Are underparticipators trying to talk or engage but getting pushed aside? Or are underparticipators waiting for overparticipators to finish and then copying their work? What kinds of participation are your underparticipators already doing well? What kinds of participation would you like to encourage in them?

Armed with your responses from your reflection, consider what forms of participation are missing in your classroom. Make a list of the forms of participation you would like to encourage. For example, you might want students to work on making sense of one another's ideas or to take turns working with manipulatives. Keep this list somewhat short. If you make a long list, you will be tempted to ask your students to take up several of these activities at once, resulting in frustration for all. Then start with one form of participation and consider which student is already adept at it.

We encourage you to pick a form of participation used by one or more of your underparticipators so that you can begin to highlight their successful participation. Consider how you might explicitly teach these ways of participating. You might model listening to and making sense of others' ideas and then have your students practice. For the next several mathematics lessons, carefully watch for examples of this form of participation and point them out to the rest of the class. Your students will need time to practice and many examples of this new participation to become proficient. As students become proficient in one new form of participation, introduce the next one on your list. You will probably need to periodically reinforce these changes in participation as your students will still hear and act on messages from outside of your classroom about how they should engage in mathematics (see chapters 7 and 8).

In closing, we reiterate that student participation, in all its forms, is central to learning mathematics. Yet it is very easy to find large inequities in our classrooms related to who participates and how. Like many inequities in our society, these differences can go unnoticed because they are hidden by beliefs about what it means to be good at math, who can be good at math, and the best ways to learn math (see chapters 1 and 3). As we examine our beliefs about participation in mathematics, we can start to see the importance of supporting each of our students in participating in ways that challenge their mathematical skills, pushing them into new ways of participating while also building their mathematical confidence. As a result, students like Dominica may find that they can do more than read questions and students like Javier may turn to peers and ask them for their ideas and solutions. Together, when our students maximize one another's opportunities for participation, they will realize NCTM's goal of access and equity for all.

References

Boaler, Jo. *Mathematical Mindsets: Unleashing Students' Potential through Creative Math, Inspiring Messages and Innovative Teaching.* San Francisco, Calif.: Jossey-Bass, 2015.

Cohen, Elizabeth G., and Rachel A. Lotan. *Designing Groupwork: Strategies for the Heterogeneous Classroom.* 3rd ed. New York: Teachers College Press, 2014.

Featherstone, Helen, Sandra Crespo, Lisa M. Jilk, Joy A. Oslund, Amy Noelle Parks, and Marcy B. Wood. *Smarter Together! Collaboration and Equity in the Elementary Math Classroom.* Reston, Va.: National Council of Teachers of Mathematics, 2011.

Lack, Brian, Susan Lee Swars, and Barbara Meyers. "Low- and High-Achieving Sixth-Grade Students' Access to Participation during Mathematics Discourse." *Elementary School Journal* 115, no. 1 (2014): 97–123.

National Council of Teachers of Mathematics (NCTM). *Principles to Actions: Ensuring Mathematical Success for All.* Reston, Va.: NCTM, 2014.

CHAPTER 10

Professional Development to Support "Integrated" Language and Mathematics Instruction for English Language Learners

Rodrigo J. Gutiérrez, *University of Maryland, College Park*

Galina (Halla) Jmourko, *Prince George's County Public Schools, Upper Marlboro, Maryland*

Consider the following words from Natalie (all names in this chapter are pseudonyms), a third-grade teacher of primarily English language learners in her mainstream classroom:

> It's hard . . . That's how I felt for a long time. I've heard these things about student engagement a lot, I've seen these things a lot, I've never tried them. Then what happens if I just commit and just try it? And now every day, we have our routines and we have to be consistent and they go across subjects. We have expectations and the children have to know them regardless of the content area: This is how we behave, this is how we respect each other, this is how we talk.

What does Natalie mean by "this is how we talk"? What does this behavior and talk look like in mathematics? What are the implications for English language learners (ELLs)?

These questions were addressed by a yearlong professional development aimed at supporting elementary teachers in engaging ELL students in mathematical discourse. By bringing mainstream and teachers of ESOL English for speakers of other languages (ESOL) together, this professional development promoted the sharing and advancement of knowledge and skills for integrating language and mathematics instruction. Participants considered and experimented with task selection, classroom norms and routines, assessment, questioning strategies, and talk moves. As a result, teachers established classroom environments that promoted active participation by ELL students in language-rich mathematics activities. Natalie describes what this looked like in her classroom:

> When you commit to having these types of discussions, it takes a while but comes naturally to the point of having children switch naturally from talking in pairs to four talking together, and they are on task for more than a minute. It's something that might seem impossible, but when they are used to it and when they know those are the expectations, they do it. They listen to each other and they respond and clarify what others are saying. It's amazing to watch them be engaged with something for that long, with each other for so long, and commit to a task and use everything they know to make you understand.

Natalie's quotations illustrate her appreciation of, and amazement at, the great progress achieved by her students after implementing several reforms to her instruction of mathematics. She shared these comments during one of the professional development sessions in the second half of the school year. Natalie's intent was to communicate to her colleagues the shifts in her professional knowledge, beliefs, and practices as she aimed to integrate language instruction into her mathematics lessons. Central to her comments was a message for colleagues to reflect on their own instruction, to raise their expectations for ELL students, and to take the necessary risks to experiment with the ideas put forth in the professional development:

> Breaking our habits is the hardest thing. We all have our lesson plans and what we've been doing for so long. What held me back for so long is just thinking of how I'm going to do everything from scratch.

Supported by the professional development structure and activities, and possibly inspired by Natalie's charge, teachers took great strides in reforming their instruction. The following sections of this chapter will provide an overview of the professional development that these teachers experienced, as well as describe the shifts in teacher instruction from an "isolated" to an "integrated" approach to addressing both language and mathematics together. It is our intention to offer a possible approach and tools for supporting teachers' professional growth as they strive to improve mathematics instruction for ELL students.

Making a Commitment to Access and Equity

While Natalie offered an inspirational account of her new understanding of instruction as a result of our professional development, Debra's description of her fourth-grade classroom below refers to typical mathematics teaching challenges before our professional development and raises questions about how to encourage children to talk in the mathematics classroom.

> I felt that my instruction was too narrow and disjointed. I was teaching the way I was taught. . . . My focus and strategies went all over the place, probably without research-based foundation. . . . How do you get kids to talk?

The challenge of getting students to talk in mathematics class is often related to the teachers' belief that "students should be taught as they [teachers] were taught, through memorizing facts, formulas, and procedures and then practicing skills over and over again" (NCTM 2014, p. 9). This outdated view of instruction creates a major obstacle to developing conceptual understanding and problem-solving skills and to promoting student interactions and discourse. When the instructional focus is mainly on the mathematics and students' use of the English language is left unattended in mathematics classrooms, opportunities are often missed for ELL students to develop their English language skills. Instead of overemphasizing mastery of the formal mathematics register at the expense of acknowledging students' mathematical understanding and reasoning (Moschkovich 2012), teachers should create opportunities for students to actively communicate mathematical ideas. Moreover, the Common Core State Standards for Mathematical Practice (CCSSMP) and WIDA's English Language Development Standards (details below) have raised the bar for the use of language in mathematics by ELL students and therefore have raised expectations for teachers to advance ELL students' language skills in tandem with mathematics. Even though participants in our professional development understood that classroom discourse can help reveal students' mathematical thinking and promote language development, they faced tremendous challenges in helping English learners access mathematical content while communicating mathematical ideas in English as a new language.

Isolated Approach

From our previous work with teachers, we observed that teachers' attempts to provide ELL students with access to mathematics and classroom communication were commonly limited to language-based activities used in isolation from meaningful mathematics activities. Teachers' "isolated" approaches to ELL students' language development and classroom participation generally included frontloading mathematical terms, supporting the language of procedural fluency, and incorporating conversational starters and prompts. While these can be considered useful instructional strategies, the examples below demonstrate how they can present limitations to students' learning and discourse skills.

We observed that teachers who frontloaded mathematical terms generally used a graphic organizer known as the Frayer model for building student vocabulary (Frayer, Frederick, and Klausmeier 1969), word-definition matching activities, or word walls, on which they posted terms and corresponding definitions. These activities, when supported by visuals and real-life examples, may provide opportunities for students to review key mathematical terms. However, when used as the sole vocabulary support and not coupled with mathematical exploration, they do not help students, particularly English learners, to commit the meanings of the vocabulary to their long-term memory. As a result, students continue to grope for words when they are expected to engage in more sophisticated mathematical practices, such as the CCSSMP's "attend to precision" and "construct viable arguments" (NGA Center and CCSSO 2010). Consequently, teachers often interpret students' limited responses as lack of mathematics skills or as disinterest in class participation.

Another example of an "isolated" practice is when the linking words that support procedural fluency are taught without emphasizing conceptual understanding. Although linking, or transition, words are commonly used to help students connect ideas in writing or orally, their use in the mathematics classroom is often limited to sequential organization (e.g., *first, next, then, last*) of the discourse around computations and procedural fluency, rather than more sophisticated words and phrases (e.g., *given that, provided that, unless, furthermore*) that advance the language skills necessary to engage in mathematical practices.

In addition to the challenges of implementing language-based supports, we observed that teachers had limited opportunities for collaboration and professional growth. Even when ESOL and mainstream teachers planned and taught together, their contributions to planning and instruction were defined by the parameters of their professional domains or roles. For example, an ESOL teacher may be strictly responsible for developing mathematical vocabulary, while the mainstream teacher selects and implements the main mathematical activities.

Call to Action for ELL Students

Considering these challenges that teachers face in promoting discourse for English learners, our commitment to access and equity for ELL students in mathematics is based on our firm belief that providing language development support to ELL students in the mathematics classrooms should neither be left to chance nor happen occasionally, but should become a sustained practice coupled with mathematics learning. We agree with this statement from NCTM's *Principles to Actions: Ensuring Mathematical Success for All* (2014): "We need to take actions to ensure that all students become confident in their ability to learn and use mathematics" (p. 109). For ELL students, this means that we need to take actions to develop and advance their language skills so that they become more capable and confident in their ability to use English to learn and use mathematics. *Principles to Actions* also states:

> We need to take actions to create classrooms and learning environments where students are actively engaged with worthwhile tasks that promote mathematical understanding, problem solving, and reasoning, . . . students are working collaboratively . . . using a range of . . . resources. They are interacting with one another and with their teacher, and they are focused on making sense of mathematics. (p. 109)

To apply these statements to working with ELL students means that we need to take actions not only to use multiple representations to help ELL students access tasks and engage with others but also to capitalize on mathematics contexts as language learning opportunities in order to address English learners' long-term language development needs. In other words, teachers must use the context of mathematical activity as a resource for developing and advancing ELL students' language skills alongside mathematics learning.

Educating ELL students is no longer the sole responsibility of ESOL teachers. All educators, including principals, coaches, and mainstream teachers, "hold collective responsibility" for the language and mathematics learning of these students. Therefore, our goal in developing this professional development was to bring mainstream and ESOL teachers together to address the needs of English learners in the mathematics classroom. More specifically, our aim was to move teachers from "isolated" attempts to develop language to an "integrated" approach where teachers—

- understand the intertwined nature of language and mathematics learning;

- view mathematics contexts as a resource for planning language development opportunities alongside mathematical learning; and

- engage in collaborative practices that raise accountability for their individual and collective professional growth,

and where students—

- use social, academic, and mathematics-specific language at the same time;

- advance in their use of language for a variety of purposes through authentic interaction with others and based on specific mathematical contexts; and

- make sense of mathematics through authentic use of language and nonlinguistic representations.

This chapter offers details on how the design, foundations, and specific practices of our professional development supported the implementation of this "integrated" approach in the classroom.

Advancing Access and Equity

Professional Development Overview: Focus Group

Guided by our commitment to access and equity, we designed a professional development experience for mainstream and ESOL elementary classroom teachers. We chose a focus-group model where a cohort of teachers would engage in sustained, ongoing professional development activities exploring one major topic. In this case, the Engaging ELLs in Mathematical Discourse Focus Group explored the development of both mathematics and language with ELL students. Our cohort consisted of twenty-five teachers (grades 2–6) who came together for seven full-day focus group sessions during the 2014–2015 school year. These teachers worked in elementary classrooms with high numbers of ELL students, in a district with large and growing numbers of students designated for ESOL services (19,203 students enrolled in ESOL in 2014–2015).

The focus group was different from previous district professional development initiatives, which either met only a handful of times or occurred after school. It also represented the first time that professional development was cofacilitated by a district employee (ESOL coach) and a university faculty member (mathematics education). By complementing each other's knowledge and resources, we aimed to model the "integrated" approach that mainstream and ESOL teachers can bring to their planning and instruction. This approach included our collaboration on the selection and sharing of research-based resources and materials that would speak to the participants' specific needs and context. Furthermore, focus-group participants benefited from personalized onsite support from the facilitators at least twice during the school year, which included assistance with planning, instruction, videotaping, and debriefing of lessons.

Each focus group session included four components: Mathematics Pedagogy, Language Development, Show-and-Tell, and Collaborative Planning Time. Before addressing the first two components, we would like to look at the latter two components, which emphasize teacher collaboration and sharing. As the name suggests, Collaborative Planning Time gave teachers a chance to engage with one another in discussions and sharing of materials as they planned for implementation of focus-group ideas in their own classrooms. Show-and-Tell allowed teachers to share in small groups about their experiences with this implementation, including newly created materials, student artifacts, classroom video, and takeaways from their curricular and instructional experimentation. In addition, some teachers shared their innovations and new understandings with the entire group.

The Mathematics Pedagogy and Language Development components were directly informed by particular principles and practices in both disciplines, partially because of recent state adoption of school content standards and language development standards. More specifically, the Mathematics Pedagogy component was strongly influenced by the Common Core State Standards for Mathematics (CCSSM) content and practice standards (NGA Center and CCSSO 2010), as well as the National Council of Teachers of Mathematics (NCTM) Teaching Practices (NCTM 2014). Additionally, the Language Development component emphasized the WIDA English Language Development Standards (see www.wida.us). Together, these sets of standards promote language development across the content areas and emphasize the role of language in mathematics. The following sections provide more details on the principles and practices central to these two components, as well as activities and instructional tools used to promote an integrated approach to developing both mathematics and language.

Mathematics Pedagogy Component: Principles, Practices, and Activities

The focus group intended to develop not only teachers' understanding of mathematical content but also their pedagogical skills for assessing student understanding, building on student thinking, and facilitating productive classroom discourse. This vision of effective mathematics teaching aligned with NCTM's *Principles to Actions* and informed the design of focus-group activities that emphasized "principles of learning that provide the foundation for effective mathematics teaching" (NCTM 2014, p. 9). More specifically, these principles call for classroom experiences where students—

- engage with challenging tasks that involve active meaning making and support meaningful learning;

- connect new learning with prior knowledge and informal reasoning and, in the process, address preconceptions and misconceptions;

- acquire conceptual knowledge as well as procedural fluency, so that they can meaningfully organize their knowledge, acquire new knowledge, and transfer and apply knowledge to new situations;

- construct knowledge socially, through discourse, activity, and interaction related to meaningful problems;

- receive descriptive and timely feedback so that they can reflect and revise their work, thinking, and understandings; and

- develop metacognitive awareness of themselves as learners, thinkers, problem solvers, and learn to monitor their learning and performance. (NCTM 2014, p. 9)

To support this vision, participants were introduced to and regularly considered both the Common Core State Standards for Mathematical Practice and NCTM's Mathematics Teaching Practices. Specific Teaching Practices were noted as being of particular importance for mathematics instruction with ELL students because they create opportunities for students to communicate mathematical ideas while developing language (i.e., use and connect mathematical representations, facilitate meaningful mathematical discourse, pose purposeful questions, elicit and use evidence of student thinking).

In order to emphasize the CCSSMPs, focus-group activities addressed mathematical content, pedagogical content knowledge, and instructional tools to promote mathematical discourse. Topics included problem solving–based mathematics, Cognitively Guided Instruction (CGI), number-sense games, mathematics talk and discourse moves, and using children's literature for teaching mathematics. To illustrate, two focus-group sessions included activities concerning CGI problem types and student strategies (Carpenter et al. 2014). These included a role-play activity where teachers acted out the semantic and computational interpretations of story problems with arithmetic operations (Bahr and DeGarcia 2008). Teachers also watched and discussed videos of clinical interviews with children and classroom instruction depicting student sharing and group discussions. Such activities helped participants develop a nuanced understanding of students' mathematical development and provided examples of student-centered teaching.

In addition to addressing pedagogical content knowledge, a significant amount of time was dedicated to examining the role of discourse in the mathematics classroom. For example, the Bag of Marbles task (Smith et al. 2009) introduced teachers to Smith and Stein's (2011) *5 Practices for Orchestrating Productive Mathematics Discussions.* This framework helped teachers see the value of anticipating student responses in order to select, sequence, and connect students' contributions to classroom activity. Furthermore, teachers investigated the effect of different patterns of questioning (Herbel-Eisenmann and Breyfogle 2005) and "Five Productive Talk Moves" (Chapin, O'Connor, and Anderson 2009). Ultimately, the explicit focus on the importance of discourse in the mathematics classroom provided a research-based foundation for connecting mathematics instruction with language development.

Language Development Component: The Language of Mathematics

In our state, instruction and assessment of ELL students follow the WIDA Standards Framework for language development, which sets expectations for development of "the social, instructional, and academic language that students need to engage with peers, educators, and the curriculum in schools" (WIDA 2014, p. 4). In particular, WIDA's English Language Development Standard 3 (the language of Mathematics) refers to students' ability to "communicate information, ideas and concepts necessary for academic success in the content area of Mathematics." (p. 4) Furthermore, WIDA's Can Do Philosophy states that all learners bring valuable cultural and life experiences and ways of learning to the classroom (p. 3). Therefore, it is important for teachers to know not only what and how they are teaching (i.e., content and pedagogy) but also who they are teaching. Instruction should begin with knowledge of students, their family and cultural backgrounds, academic skills, learning styles, personalities, and interests. For ELL students, it is essential to know and understand their English language proficiency levels, including proficiency levels in speaking, listening, reading, and writing.

Based on the view of language as a tool for learning and communication, WIDA's standards outline specific criteria for the use of language in a variety of sociocultural contexts for specific purposes and across different learning environments. In particular, WIDA defines vocabulary, language forms and conventions, and linguistic complexity as features of the academic language in any content area, including mathematics. Under these criteria, ELL students have to meet expectations for comprehension and the use of language at

---

word, sentence, and discourse levels in order to become proficient in English. It is worth emphasizing that WIDA characterizes *discourse* as a linguistically complex feature that shows students' ability to organize information in a specific structure according to a specific purpose. WIDA's definition of and expectation for "discourse" is fundamentally different from what we know generally as "classroom discourse" (e.g., an exchange of words, phrases, or even gestures).

To guide instruction for ELL students, WIDA provides Can Do Descriptors (Gottlieb, Cranley, and Cammilleri 2007) with useful information about the type of tasks that English learners can engage in at different stages of language development and in a variety of academic contexts. Furthermore, WIDA emphasizes the importance of teachers employing instructional supports "to assist students in accessing content necessary for classroom understanding or communication" (Gottlieb, Cranley, and Cammilleri 2007, p. 20). For example, WIDA suggests three types of commonly used supports: sensory (e.g., pictures, diagrams, manipulatives); graphic (e.g., graphic organizers, charts, number lines); and interactive (e.g., in pairs, in triads, in a small group). These supports were a central feature of the focus group, as we introduced teachers to specific instructional tools that aimed to integrate mathematics and language development.

Integrated Approach

In order to address both language and mathematics development, we searched for ways in which the WIDA standards framework aligned with NCTM's vision of effective mathematics instruction. We identified several interrelated features that overlapped the two frameworks, allowing for instruction that integrates language and mathematics learning. For example, both WIDA and NCTM call for instruction that relates to students' languages, cultures, and life experiences and that allows students to construct (mathematical) meaning in a variety of ways. Furthermore, both promote classroom discourse where students use everyday, academic (i.e., across the content areas), and mathematics-specific English, often in combination with other representations (e.g., visual, graphic, numeric, symbolic).

An integrated approach to addressing these instructional goals emphasizes that mathematics activities can be resources for language development and that language-rich activities can further mathematical understanding. This bi-directionality allows for interactive classroom activities with authentic use of language for different purposes in different mathematical contexts, supporting students' understanding of mathematics and use of language when communicating mathematical ideas. To help teachers implement this approach, we expanded on WIDA's recommendations for language supports for ELL students and created a new comprehensive framework (see fig. 10.1) to inform teachers' planning and instruction.

Language Development Supports For English Language Learners To Increase Comprehension and Communication Skills

Environment

- Welcoming and stress-free
- Respectful of linguistic and cultural diversity
- Honors students' background knowledge
- Sets clear and high expectations
- Includes routines and norms
- Is thinking-focused vs. answer-seeking
- Offers multiple modalities to engage in content learning and to demonstrate understanding
- Includes explicit instruction of specific language targets
- Provides participation techniques to include all learners

- Integrates learning centers and games in a meaningful way
- Provides opportunities to practice and refine receptive and productive skills in English as a new language
- Integrates meaning and purposeful tasks/activities that:
  - Are accessible by all students through multiple entry points
  - Are relevant to students' lives and cultural experiences
  - Build on prior mathematical learning
  - Demonstrate high cognitive demand
  - Offer multiple strategies for solutions
  - Allow for a language learning experience in addition to content

Sensory Supports*	Graphic Supports*	Interactive Supports*	Verbal and Textual Supports
<ul><li>Real-life objects (realia) or concrete objects</li><li>Physical models</li><li>Manipulatives</li><li>Pictures & photographs</li><li>Visual representations or models such as diagrams or drawings</li><li>Videos & films</li><li>Newspapers or magazines</li><li>Gestures</li><li>Physical movements</li><li>Music & songs</li></ul>	<ul><li>Graphs</li><li>Charts</li><li>Timelines</li><li>Number lines</li><li>Graphic organizers</li><li>Graphing paper</li></ul>	<ul><li>In a whole group</li><li>In a small group</li><li>With a partner such as *Turn-and-Talk*</li><li>In pairs as a group (first, two pairs work independently, then they form a group of four)</li><li>In triads</li><li>Cooperative learning structures such as *Think-Pair-Share*</li><li>Interactive websites or software</li><li>With a mentor or coach</li></ul>	<ul><li>Labeling</li><li>Students' native language</li><li>Modeling</li><li>Repetitions</li><li>Paraphrasing</li><li>Summarizing</li><li>Guiding questions</li><li>Clarifying questions</li><li>Probing questions</li><li>Leveled questions such as *What? When? Where? How? Why?*</li><li>Questioning prompts & cues</li><li>Word Banks</li><li>Sentence starters</li><li>Sentence frames</li><li>Discussion frames</li><li>Talk moves, including *Wait Time*</li></ul>

*from *Understanding the WIDA English Language Proficiency Standards. A Resource Guide*. 2007 Edition. Board of Regents of the University of Wisconsin System, on behalf of the WIDA Consortium—www.wida.us.

Fig. 10.1. Language development supports for English language learners to increase comprehension and communication skills

Instructional Tools

Throughout the focus group, teachers explored a variety of different instructional tools designed to apply these language-development supports during mathematics instruction. The implementation of these instructional tools helped teachers see the benefits of using an integrated approach to address the challenges and expectations for language development while also promoting student engagement in mathematical practices. These tools also helped teachers assess both mathematical understanding and language use during class activities, and then respond to students' needs by appropriately differentiating instruction. The following sections provide examples of two instructional tools that teachers were introduced to and experimented with. We highlight the use of these tools with English learners since they explicitly promote language development in the following ways:

- Allow for practice of receptive and productive language skills

- Help organize thinking by connecting or simplifying ideas

- Allow for integration of multiple representations to reveal student mathematical thinking and support use of language

- Allow for language development and modifications at a word level, sentence level, and discourse level to meet the needs of students of different language proficiency levels

- Purposefully emphasize use of language, such as different types of vocabulary and different types of sentence structure to enhance and refine (mathematical) communication skills

Three-Way Tie. Adapted from a mathematics summarizing tool, Three-Way Tie (Silver, Brunsting, and Walsh 2008) provides multiple opportunities for developing and advancing students' oral and written discourse skills. This graphic support uses a triangular representation to connect three mathematical terms or concepts chosen by the teacher or students. Not only do students use words and drawings to connect topics along each side of the triangle, but they may also provide a synthesis in the triangle's center. Such an open-ended tool allows for student sense-making, communication, and representation, without overscaffolding language use. Student writing and representations not only communicate their understanding of the relationships between these concepts but also allow the teacher to assess both mathematics and language development.

Figure 10.2 depicts a third-grade ELL student using Three-Way Tie to explore the concepts of area and perimeter. Given three mathematical terms (*area*, *perimeter*, and *square*), the student constructed sentences about three relationships: area-perimeter, perimeter-square, and area-square. Analysis of this work elucidates several language-development benefits of using Three-Way Tie:

Use of basic words (e.g., *inside* and *outside*) in combination with mathematical terms (e.g., *area, perimeter, measures*) to construct meaningful sentences (e.g., "Area measures inside the perimeter because perimeter measures the outside of a shape.").

Risk-taking and experimentation with language when focused on specific mathematical concepts. For example, the sentence "In a square there are the equal area and divided by 4 equal pieces" exemplifies the student taking risks to step out of the formal word order by beginning a sentence with "In a square" and by extending the meaning of the word *area*.

Use of drawings or representations as evidence of mathematical thinking and as support when students are still struggling to use English as a new language.

Further analysis also provides valuable information about the mathematical benefits of this instructional tool. Using mathematical vocabulary within defined concept parameters provides students with an opportunity to engage

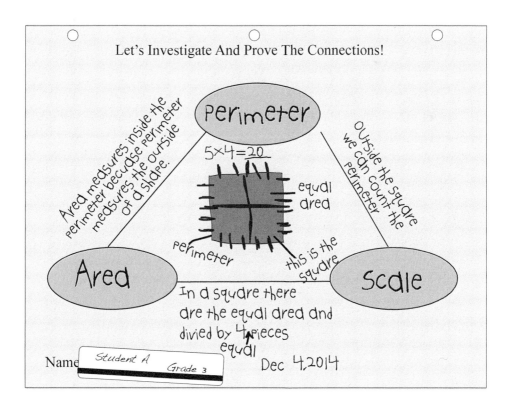

Fig. 10.2. Example of student work with Three-Way Tie

in mathematical practices, such as "construct viable arguments" and "attend to precision" (NGA Center and CCSSO 2010), as it prompts students to be thoughtful about the use of vocabulary and sentence structure in order to make sense mathematically. In additional, students' writing showed their general understanding of how area and perimeter relate to each other mathematically. However, examples from other students' work (e.g., "We count the square units to find out the area." "We used marks to find out the perimeter of a square.") revealed students' tendency to apply a procedural approach when describing the relationship between area and perimeter. In turn, this information provides teachers with an opportunity to assess students' language skills and mathematical understanding in order to identify possible next steps. In this case, the teacher can introduce and explore two-dimensional figures other than a square to help students refine their language and understanding of perimeter and area, without focusing on procedures for calculation. Furthermore, the teacher can inquire into Student A's use of hash marks in the drawing (see fig. 10.2) in order to better understand the counting or measurement approach.

The graphic design of the Three-Way Tie tool reinforces student understanding of the interconnectedness of mathematical concepts. While promoting student meaning-making and connections among concepts, the tool also supports ELL students in becoming more proficient users of language when they select vocabulary, grammar forms, and language structures to make their mathematical ideas meaningful and comprehensible.

Cubing Game. To fully engage in academic discourse, ELL students need to develop the ability to use language for different purposes, as determined by the mathematical tasks. In other words, ELL students need to know not only *what* to talk about, but also *how* to talk about it. To illustrate, Bresser, Melanese, and Sphar (2009) stated: "As there are purposes for the various strands in mathematics, so are there purposes, or functions, for language. We use language to describe, to compare, to contrast, to predict, to categorize" (p. 166).

The Cubing Game (Altieri 2010) allows ELL students to practice the use of these language functions through an interactive game that encourages students to talk or write about a concept with different purposes (e.g., *describe, apply, compare/contrast, connect/associate, create, define*). Students roll a cube with a different academic word on each face and then create a sentence to communicate the resulting perspective in relation to a specific concept. For example, students may need to compare area and perimeter. In this case, "compare" requires a certain structure (i.e., "__ is the same as __") and the use of linking words (e.g., *similarly* and *both*).

The Cubing Game is a challenging activity that requires careful planning and preparation to meet the needs of students of different language proficiency levels. In order to address the needs of individual students or classes, this tool can be modified by explicitly incorporating a sentence and a list of academic words for language functions at the beginning to draw students' attention to the purpose of the task at hand; providing a list of guiding questions to focus students' thinking and orient responses around different language functions and perspectives (see fig. 10.3); providing visual cues specific for each of the language functions and perspectives; providing sentence starters and frames to support language structures associated with specific language functions; and providing a word bank of key mathematical terms associated with the concept. Ultimately, the Cubing Game tool offers an engaging opportunity for ELL students to practice using academic language explicitly embedded in the language functions while fostering their higher-order thinking skills.

As shown in figure 10.3, fourth-grade ELL students explored fractions by using the Cubing Game with guiding questions. Analysis of Student B's writing with different purposes reveals a broad understanding of fractions, as exemplified by the student's use of language (e.g., "fraction is a number," "numerator," "denominator," "dividing them between people"), real-life applications, and visual representations of fractions (i.e., number line, circular model). However, the sentences for *describe* and *define* are very similar, primarily referring to the use of a numerator and a denominator. Perhaps this lack of distinction between the two functions is a result of the linguistic and cognitive complexity that these academic words carry in mathematics. It is important to point out that "define" is of extreme importance in mathematics and necessitates precise use of language to communicate sophisticated knowledge in a concise way. To develop this distinction, the teacher can choose to provide a concrete example for students to *describe* and provide a sentence starter to support students' use of descriptive language (e.g., "__ has"). In additional, the teacher can provide specific sentence starters to scaffold understanding and use of the *define* function in a sentence (e.g., " __ is __ "; " __ is defined as __"). This would also help students realize the difference in the type of language structures used when defining or describing something mathematically.

To summarize, these instructional tools can help teachers implement an integrated instructional approach for supporting ELL students in mathematics. These tools not only help teachers assess students' use of language and mathematics but can also be adapted to target receptive or productive language skills, depending on students' language needs in relation to the mathematical goals of the lesson. Classroom implementation can be interactive in nature by offering multiple ways to engage students with a partner, in a small group,

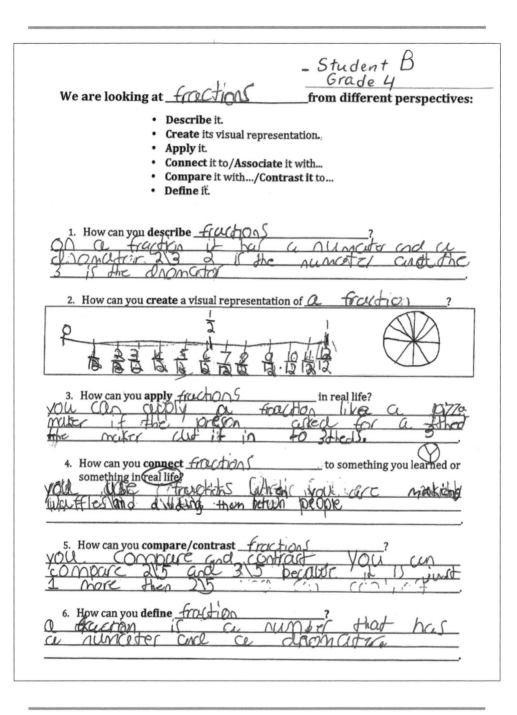

Fig. 10.3 Example of student work with Cubing Game

or with the whole class. These instructional tools offer opportunities for students to engage in cognitively demanding tasks, refine their use of language to appropriately support their mathematical reasoning and argumentation, and engage in productive mathematical practices. Ultimately, these types of instructional tools can help ELL students access the language of the mathematics classroom while they become more confident language users and mathematics learners.-

Successes: Shifts in Teachers' Instruction

After spending a substantial portion of the school year exploring the ideas from the focus group and implementing a range of instructional tools in their classroom, teachers shared and demonstrated significant shifts in their understanding of school mathematics, professional beliefs, and most important, their mathematics instruction with English learners. Through group sharing and presentations, teachers described a clearer vision of how to move from isolated vocabulary exercises to contextualized language development. They specifically noted their intentions to adapt their questioning, integrate talk moves, focus on mathematical concepts instead of procedures, integrate children's literature, and implement a variety of language-development supports. The following quotes illustrate these shifts:

> What we used to do is to frontload vocabulary and a lot of whole-class-driven instruction. We wanted the students to give us specific responses. . . . Now, we want students to discover learning. We don't frontload the vocabulary, but they are learning vocabulary as they are learning math.

> We presume that the words are too hard for them. We give them a word and presume that they won't remember it. . . . We discussed academic words such as *demonstrate, illustrate,* or *describe*; the more we use those and show what we mean by using them in context, the more they will associate the words with that meaning.

These quotes illustrate teacher shifts from isolated attempts to develop language (e.g., "frontload vocabulary") to an integrated approach where students are "learning vocabulary as they are learning math" and using language for a variety of mathematical purposes (e.g., "demonstrate, illustrate, or describe"). Partly because of their experiences in the focus group, teachers came to understand the intertwined nature of language and mathematics and began to view mathematics contexts as resources for language development alongside mathematical learning.

Additionally, teachers' efforts to implement an integrated approach to mathematics and language learning positively affected their collaborative efforts as they began to redefine their professional domains to include being both a language-development teacher and a mathematics teacher. As a result, teachers engaged in collaborative practices and collective accountability for planning and teaching ELL students (e.g., co-planning, co-teaching, professional learning communities). In this way, teachers answered NCTM's call to action to address access and equity in mathematics education by paying particular attention to the experiences, needs, and resources of ELL students.

Challenges and Considerations

Although focus-group participants validated the important work accomplished through this yearlong professional development experience, it is important to acknowledge the challenges and tensions that arose in designing and implementing the focus group.

First, such initiatives must consider the role of administration. In our case, the district had identified a curricular and instructional priority to develop students' literacy, including mathematical literacy. Therefore, the focus group was seen as being in alignment with this priority, and the ESOL department was able to provide the necessary funds (i.e., Title 3), including pay for substitutes to allow teachers to attend the full-day sessions. Furthermore, school administration (i.e., principals) allowed teachers to be absent from their classrooms on multiple days, which is not always an easy sell. Moreover, we (the designers of the focus group) also considered the importance of professional development for principals and other instructional leaders. With their leadership, entire schools can better implement an integrated approach to mathematics and language development. Perhaps future initiatives will focus more on the role of administration.

Second, the beginning of the school year is often unpredictable and rife with staffing and scheduling concerns. For example, ESOL teachers often do not finalize their caseload and schedules until several weeks into the school year. Furthermore, mainstream teachers sometimes change grade levels or subjects from year to year. These considerations made it difficult to target specific schools, grades, and classrooms and to find consistency in participants in the initial focus-group sessions.

Last, an essential component of the focus group was the personalized, onsite support by the facilitators between sessions. We found that the most productive support occurred when teachers collaborated at their school sites and included us in planning, instruction, videotaping, and debriefing. Though it would be optimal to provide such support between all sessions, this highly personalized attention may prove difficult to achieve with a larger number of participants. Perhaps district commitment to this type of professional development can result in increased numbers of instructional coaches and in focusing their workloads on fewer, targeted schools.

Reflecting and Taking Action

This chapter introduced a professional development structure (focus group) and several instructional tools for improving mathematics instruction for English language learners. We hope that you, the reader, will engage with these materials and explore ways of adapting them into your work with students and teachers. Below are a few suggestions for how teachers, administrators, and professional developers can implement such materials to provide ELL students with access to mathematics through purposeful and meaningful integration of mathematics and language development.

A central aspect of our professional development work is promoting collaboration among teachers (see chapter 11 for another professional development model that also requires partnerships of educators and administrators). Documents related to the principles, practices, and instructional strategies we have referenced can be powerful discussion starters during professional development, grade or department meetings, book circles, or team meetings. Small groups or pairs of teachers can collaboratively plan for the implementation of specific units, activities, or instructional tools. In an ESOL instructional setting, cooperating teachers can share their expertise when reviewing, discussing, and implementing language-based mathematics activities. Regardless of the context, it is essential that all teachers' knowledge and experiences be valued when cooperating. Too often, we have seen power dynamics where mainstream teachers tell the ESOL teacher what mathematics skills and terms they are to teach to ELL students, without engaging their colleague in professional decision making about what is best for the children with consideration of their English language proficiency, as well as their cultural and life experiences. Hopefully, these instructional tools provide a middle ground for teachers to bring their perspectives and suggestions as the team develops and implements a shared vision of language-rich mathematics instruction.

We also find it essential that school and district administrators develop a deep understanding of the principles and practices discussed above (i.e., CCSS Mathematical Practices, NCTM Teacher Practices, state-adopted language development standards). Only then can they be effective instructional leaders able to assess and inform teachers' mathematics instruction. Guided by these frameworks, administrators can establish regular professional development opportunities for teachers to explore and implement language-based mathematics activities. They can also support teaching pairs or teams as they collaboratively experiment with instructional tools. Ultimately, by bringing attention to the mathematics instruction of English learners, administrators can address issues of equity by creating a culture of collective responsibility and accountability for the academic success of ELL students.

It was our intention for this chapter to offer a clear example of how to structure teacher professional development focused on an integrated approach to language and mathematics instruction (see chapters 5 and 6 for more instructional strategies that integrate language and mathematics that work for ELL students). Beginning with research-based principles and practices, professional developers can support teachers to understand the expectations and possibilities of local standards and policies. Professional development activities can build teachers' content and pedagogical knowledge, consistently reinforcing the integration of mathematics and language instruction. Furthermore, teachers need time to review promising instructional tools, as well as opportunities to experiment with them in their classroom. Most important, teachers need dedicated time to collaborate with colleagues as they engage in a professional learning community. Such sustained professional development must consider the local context of the school and districts while maintaining an explicit focus on working with ELL students in mathematics. In order for professional developers to gain a comprehensive and nuanced understanding of the local educational landscape, they should spend significant amounts of time in classrooms with teachers, offering support, guidance, feedback, and suggestions. Although it may be difficult to incorporate all these components, professional developers can implement a variety of structures that offer teachers a range of experiences, with the ultimate goal of providing ELL students with access to classroom discourse through challenging, rigorous, and language-rich mathematics instruction.

References

Altieri, Jennifer L. "Strengthening Writing Skills While Communicating Mathematical Knowledge" in *Literacy + Math = Creative Connections in the Elementary Classroom*, pp. 43–66. Newark, Del.: International Reading Association, 2010.

Bahr, Damon, and Lisa Ann DeGarcia. *Elementary Mathematics Is Anything but Elementary: Content and Methods from a Developmental Perspective.* Boston: Wadsworth Cengage Learning, 2008.

Bresser, Rusty, Kathy Melanese, and Christine Sphar. *Supporting English Language Learners in Math Class.* Sausalito, Calif.: Math Solutions Publications, 2009.

Carpenter, Thomas, Elizabeth Fennema, Megan Franke, Linda Levi, and Susan Empson. *Children's Mathematics: Cognitively Guided Instruction.* Portsmouth, N.H.: Heinemann, 2014.

Chapin, Suzanne, Cathy O'Connor, and Nancy Anderson. *Classroom Discussions: Using Math Talk to Help Students Learn.* Sausalito, Calif.: Math Solutions Publications, 2009.

Frayer, Dorothy, Wayne Frederick, and Herbert Klausmeier. *A Schema for Testing the Level of Concept Mastery*. Madison, Wisc.: Wisconsin Research and Development Center for Cognitive Learning, 1969.

Gottlieb, Margo, M., Elizabeth Cranley, and Andrea Cammilleri. *Understanding the WIDA English Language Proficiency Standards: A Resource Guide*. Board of Regents of the University of Wisconsin System, on behalf of the WIDA Consortium, 2007. https://www.wida.us/standards/resource_guide_web.pdf

Herbel-Eisenmann, Beth, and M. Lynn Breyfogle. "Questioning Our Patterns of Questioning." *Mathematics Teaching in the Middle School* 10, no. 9 (2005): 484-89.

Moschkovich, Judit. "Mathematics, the Common Core, and Language: Recommendations for Mathematics Instruction for ELs Aligned with the Common Core." *Understanding Language*. Stanford, Calif.: Stanford University, 2012. http:/ell.stanford.edu/publication/mathematics-common-core-and-language

National Council of Teachers of Mathematics (NCTM). *Principles to Actions: Ensuring Mathematical Success for All*. Reston, Va.: NCTM, 2014.

National Governors Association Center for Best Practices (NGA Center) and Council of Chief State School Officials (CCSSO). *Common Core State Standards for Mathematics*. Washington, D.C.: NGA Center and CCSSO, 2010. http://www.corestandards.org

Silver, Harvey, John Brunsting, and Terry Walsh. *Math Tools, Grades 3–12: 64 Ways to Differentiate Instruction and Increase Student Engagement.* Thousand Oaks, Calif.: Corwin, 2008.

Smith, Margaret S., Elizabeth K. Hughes, Randy A. Engle, and Mary Kay Stein. "Orchestrating Discussions." *Mathematics Teaching in the Middle School* 14, no. 9 (2009): 548–56.

Smith, Margaret S., and Mary Kay Stein. *5 Practices for Orchestrating Productive Mathematics Discussions.* Reston, Va.: NCTM, 2011.

WIDA. *Understanding the WIDA English Language Proficiency Standards: A Resource Guide.* Board of Regents of the University of Wisconsin System, on behalf of the WIDA Consortium, 2007. https://www.wida.us/standards/Resource_Guide_web.pdf.

———. *2012 Amplification of the English Language Development Standards, Kindergarten-Grade 12*. Board of Regents of the University of Wisconsin System, on behalf of the WIDA Consortium, 2014. https://www.wida.us/get.aspx?id=540

CHAPTER 11

Stories from the Trenches

Urban Classrooms in Portland

Emma Ford, *Portland Public Schools, Oregon*

Brian Greer, *Portland State University*

Michael Koopman, *Portland Public Schools, Oregon*

Bijal Makadia, *Portland Public Schools, Oregon*

Swapna Mukhopadhyay, *Portland State University*

Mark Wilson, *Portland Public Schools, Oregon*

Marsha Wolfe, *Portland Public Schools, Oregon*

To honor the great diversity of languages spoken in the homes of the students in one of the schools where we work, students brought from home a single sheet of paper that said at the top "The language I speak at home is ____,"followed by "The counting words for 1–20 in my home language are ____." The response was very positive. The parents filled up the sheets, and the children were enthusiastic about sharing what they had never discussed in class before. This excitement spread among us adults as we started sharing the counting words in other languages. This ongoing discussion related to the large world map that hung in the room: In which part of the world is this language spoken? Where else is this language spoken?

To celebrate the linguistic diversity in the school, we recorded each child counting in his or her home language and created a large display in a high-traffic hallway of the school. We started with a Peters Projection World Map (on which areas are accurately represented), giving an opportunity to look at different projections and to discuss the mathematics (as well as the politics) behind map making. The pictures of the children were positioned on the map, with strings connecting where they are now to where they (and their parents) came from. The large bulletin board with the children's pictures and crisscrossing multicolored string created a strong testimony of multicultural classrooms and a visual provocation for all those who passed by.

The children recited the counting words in their home languages at first in their classrooms, where their peers listened with rapt attention. Soon these sharings spilled over to the hallways—children learning to count from one another. "I can count up to thirty in Spanish"; "Say Moja, Mbili, Tatu, ..." The list of languages spoken at home was long: Arabic, Bulgarian, English, Fulani, Kirundi, Korean, Oromo, Portuguese, Russian, Spanish, Sudanese, Swahili.

At the end of the school year, Culturally Responsive Elementary Mathematics Education (CREME) members and Rosa Parks teachers and staff organized a community gathering to showcase the students' mathematical activities. Students decorated the foyer and the hallway with banners and flags from different countries. Students and teachers displayed games from different cultures, artifacts the children made, and the talismans the children had created (see below). CREME teachers led hands-on activities at Maker tables. Children in the school orchestra provided music, on their own initiative, while parents, community members, and other students mingled. In this gala atmosphere, the map with the children's pictures showing where they are now and where they came from was a popular destination. Voices of the children, counting up to twenty in multiple home languages, were played on a loop. We had prepared handouts with counting words in all these languages for students and community members to take home. And the children, some sitting on the floor in front of the map, were listening to their own voices and the collective voice thus created. They were smiling.

Making a Commitment to Access and Equity

The vignette above comes from our project Culturally Responsive Elementary Mathematics Education (CREME). This project revolves around professional development for a small, dedicated group of teachers. At the same time, it represents our attempt to develop a conception of what culturally responsive (elementary) mathematics education might be (Greer et al. 2009). At the core of CREME is our conviction that mathematics education is not only about teaching mathematical content; everything we do is embedded in historical, cultural, social, and, indeed, political contexts. Improving mathematics education is difficult because it is a human problem, not a technical one.

What does the vignette have to say about access and equity? At first sight, the mathematical content seems appropriate to younger children, but we have deliberately chosen this experience as particularly striking to illustrate the importance of connecting mathematics in school to the students' cultural identities (Aguirre, Mayfield-Ingram, and Martin 2013). By the simple act of asking children to say number words in their home languages, we sent a message that mathematics is not something that is solely the intellectual property of English-speaking white people. Counting is both universal, in the sense that it is an activity that happens in all cultures, and culturally diverse, in that there are differences in, for example, number representations, counting devices, and cultural connotations of counting acts.

We share NCTM's commitment to access and equity, but we consider that it needs to be complemented in many respects and to be deeply and courageously interrogated by asking the fundamental kinds of questions posed by Martin (2015) in relation to "the collective Black" and more generally by Noddings (2003) who asks the most fundamental question of all: "*Why* do we teach mathematics?" (p. 87).

In *Principles to Actions: Ensuring Mathematical Success for All* (NCTM 2014) an appeal is made to "the nonnegotiable core that *ensures* that *all* students learn mathematics at *high levels*" (p. 4). We challenge the notion that it is possible to ensure that all students learn mathematics at high levels. Our challenge is based on the simple observation that in any society there are diversified roles. Likewise, we dispute the assertion that a high level of mathematics is necessary for being career or college ready. Artists and artisans, religious leaders and therapists, nurses and doctors, and on and on (the reader can easily extend the list) use very little *formal* mathematics beyond arithmetic and simple plane geometry (though we regard it as obvious that they should have access to it if they want).

Thus, a commitment to "access" needs to be accompanied by careful analysis of "access to what, and for what"; in our view, that is part of the equity issue. In this regard, we find the Common Core State Standards for Mathematics (National Governors Association Center for Best Practices and Council of Chief State School Officers [NGA Center and CCSSO] 2010) problematic in many respects. These points are particularly relevant to this chapter:

- The word *culture* and its cognates are strikingly absent from the document, nor is there any indication that the creation of mathematics as a discipline is anything other than solely a European achievement.

- CCSSM and associated documentation are written in stilted, overformal language, exacerbating the problems of teachers trying to teach, in particular, children for whom English is not their first language. This style also contributes to the remarkable failure of the document to convey that learning mathematics could be enjoyable and interesting.

Further, we see a fundamental disconnect between the forms of summative assessment to which children are subjected and the admirable two pages at the start of CCSSM listing eight key mathematical practices, including argumentation and modeling. Such essentially social practices cannot be assessed adequately through mass tests on paper or computer screens. They require clarification through dialogue in interactions among students and teachers. Moreover, the collection of computer-written responses discriminates against students whose first language is not English and those with limited computer skills. And we have no confidence that those who are employed to interpret what is written can do so reliably. In general, if assessment items refer to aspects of social reality, they are not independent of cultural knowledge and therefore not equitable; this is a ubiquitous and unavoidable problem for mass-market textbooks and mass-administered assessments.

As the preceding critique makes clear, discussion of mathematics education cannot be separated from broader contexts of educational and social politics. During our project, for example, we have become acutely aware of the tension for immigrants between the practicalities of day-to-day existence in the course of adapting to a new society and the maintenance of cultural identity. Waiting at the bus stop near one of the schools in our project or stopping at the corner store, one sees the community as a very diverse group of recent immigrants (Sottile 2015). People dress in different ways and speak in different languages, and all are trying to adapt to their new environment. In English language development, the immigrant children are best supported when their bicultural identities are nurtured, helping them navigate effectively in multiple cultural and social worlds. Schools as formal cultural institutions play a strong role in shaping the identities of the children. Immigrant children with their unique socio-emotional needs, and by implication their parents and community, get to realize the role of the context of the school in defining and valorizing certain activities—such as emphasis on and performance in standardized testing—that often fail to acknowledge and valorize their own rich cultural and linguistic assets as they try to assimilate in the larger, host culture. The stripping away of cultural identity is a threat for immigrant children. They often grow up disengaged from academic learning and disillusioned about school, thus not attaining their fullest potential as contributing members of society (Oregon Education Investment Board, Oregon Education Association, and Oregon Department of Education 2015).

On a positive note, we have recently seen a number of highly encouraging developments within our state, Oregon. The Oregon Department of Education (ODE) funded a dozen or so projects (including CREME) through the Culturally Responsive Pedagogy and Practices Grant, which had as its stated mission to work toward forming a culturally responsive teaching force in the state. In June 2015, the Oregon Education Investment Board, the Oregon Education Association, and the Oregon Department of Education published a new path for Oregon, a document that contends that the balance of assessment should be switched from summative to formative. it pays particular attention to "culturally responsive assessment," as this example shows:

> A successful system of assessment should not simply highlight problems or generalize about groups; nor should it ignore conditions that influence performance. Instead, a successful system of assessment recognizes the myriad strengths of various learners within their respective communities and within the collaborative nature of the classroom. In addition, such a system is culturally responsive, and implemented by teachers who are assessment literate. (p. 8)

Advancing Access and Equity

A leading proponent of culturally responsive teaching, Geneva Gay, asked: "How can the general principles of culturally responsive teaching be applied in practice in mathematics education?" (Gay 2009, p. 189). We emphasize that such a commitment needs to start in elementary school, at a time when children's dispositions toward and conceptions of mathematics, as well as their identities as cultural beings and as learners, are being formed.

The professional development within CREME differs from many such endeavors in being long-term and based on building a foundation of trust, a safe space for honest and deep discussions, with a small group of teachers in two schools in North Portland. Though less than three miles apart, the schools contrast in many respects. One (which will be called School A) serves a diverse population of children, many of whom are recent immigrants who have experienced trauma (Sottile 2015; see also chapter 4). The other (School B) is a public charter school that is based on progressive principles and is part of the Portland Public School system. Its student population is largely white.

Over two years (and still continuing), the authors of this chapter have met regularly and have built a strong foundation of mutual respect and solidarity. The program includes these central elements:

- The academicians, together with colleagues, including project advisers, have introduced the teachers to work on defining and implementing culturally responsive mathematics education.

- Through discussions and many classroom visits, the teachers and the students have provided the academicians with a reality check about the conditions in the schools and more generally in the communities they serve. Moreover, they have reinforced in the academicians the conviction that teaching and learning are, above all, about caring relationships. (Kitchen et al. 2006)

- Students and teachers have engaged in interactions between the two schools.

- Beginning attempts have been made to engage the communities; we see this effort as a long-term process dependent on the establishment of trust.

- We have drawn on local resources (see the examples below).

During the meetings, we have discussed many inspiring writings and recorded talks, including those of the three scholar activists who immediately agreed to be advisers for the project: Marta Civil, Geneva Gay, and Danny Martin. We also benefited from multiple face-to-face and Skype discussions with these scholar activists. In the early months of the project, the group focused on fostering reflection and expanding the teachers' thinking about access, equity, identity, and agency in teaching and learning mathematics. We discussed mathematics as a multicultural subject, with emphasis on the cultural perspective. For example, we drew on Bishop's (1988) six classes of mathematical activities that happen in essentially all cultures, namely, counting, measuring, locating, designing, playing, and explaining. A major emphasis has been the concept of ethnomathematics (D'Ambrosio 1985; Mukhopadhyay and Greer 2012), which has two important aspects (Powell and Frankenstein 1997):

- Constructing a narrative that counters the dominant perception of mathematics as the intellectual achievement of Europeans only.

- Acknowledging nonacademic mathematical practices in all cultures (e.g., Zaslavsky 1973).

Of particular relevance is the concept of "funds of knowledge" (Civil 2007; González, Moll, and Amanti 2005), which is "based on a simple premise: People are competent, they have knowledge, and their life experiences have given them that knowledge" (González, Moll, and Amanti 2005, p. ix). As an example, we studied Sandoval-Taylor's (2005) account of her development of a curriculum module for a second-grade bilingual class composed mainly of Native American and Hispanic students that was based on the theme of local building construction (discussed also in Civil 2002, 2007). We later had the opportunity to talk about this work with Sandoval-Taylor when she visited our class.

More recently, Esteban-Guitart and Moll (2014) developed a related concept, "funds of identity," which they introduced in this way:

> We use the term funds of identity to refer to the historically accumulated, culturally developed, and socially distributed resources that are essential for a person's self-definition, self-expression, and self-understanding. Funds of knowledge—bodies of knowledge and skills that are essential for the well-being of an entire household— become funds of identity when people actively use them to define themselves. (p. 31)

This statement provides a concise justification for the emphasis that we put on identity work in CREME and in this chapter.

We have also extensively discussed assessment, using as a key text *Embedded Formative Assessment* (Wiliam 2011), as well as papers from a growing literature on culturally responsive assessment, particularly in relation to mathematics.

To illustrate one of Bishop's (1988) categories—designing—and to draw on local resources, CREME teachers visited the Portland Art Museum, which has a major collection of Native American artifacts. Textiles and ceramics offer many examples of complex designs relating, in particular, to the mathematical concepts of symmetry and tessellation. We also organized field trips for students to Portland State University, during which children interacted with students and faculty in architecture, engineering, and earth sciences.

School B has a tradition of working through Storyline projects, an approach primarily developed in Scotland in which students, together with their teacher, create characters within a setting and then explore a given story in depth. Koopman (2017) describes such a project that began with students looking at the labels on their t-shirts to see where they were made. The places were recorded with pins on a world map. Koopman reports that looking at the concentrations of pins in particular areas came as a revelation, even to him. From there, the class collectively did extensive research about the factories where t-shirts were originally made in the early 1900s. By using historical data (such as prices of groceries), they calculated the cost of living for a family at that time in relation to the pay that a factory worker received. They took on roles of workers and factory owners and acted out situations of conflict (Koopman related the conflicts enacted by the students to his own experiences during a teacher strike when he was coerced by the school district to substitute for striking teachers).

The project culminated with research into contemporary conditions for workers in sweatshops in countries such as Bangladesh.

Another project involved students building models of food carts (for which Portland is famous). Students created characters for the cart owners and operators and devised detailed business models. They filled in actual forms relating to hygiene requirements for these simulated businesses. Koopman posted reviews on Yelp.

In these and similar projects, a great deal of arithmetic was done in context, illustrating how, in elementary school, students may—

- be introduced to the conception of mathematics as a tool for interrogating sociopolitical issues, thus appreciating at an early age a sense of critical agency that will stand them in good stead as citizens;

- consolidate computational and planning skills in complex contexts that afford relevance, interest, and motivation; and

- learn and practice mathematics integrated with other school subjects (science, obviously, but also art, social studies, and language arts)— something that elementary teachers are in the best position to do.

A guiding principle of our approach is to combat deficit models—those in which a negative message is conveyed to children about their intellectual capabilities, the most direct medium being test scores. Other, more subtle messages convey the less tangible effects of differential cultural capital (Yosso 2005).

Instead, we emphasize asset pedagogy, in particular through identity work, one aspect of which is self-evaluation. We use a simple activity that involves the children recording what they know they can do. They are given a length of blank adding machine tape and record "I can do" statements, deliberately left unstructured so as to provide a holistic perspective for children. As a result, the lists naturally consist of nonacademic categories sprinkled in with the academic ones. For a child, being able to "skateboard backward," "give bath to a baby sister," or "play ukulele" is as important a part of his or her identity as "do multiplication" and "read chapter books."

The children roll up this paper and store it in an empty, recycled medicine bottle that serves as a talisman. They decorate their talismans and add more lists on an ongoing basis. A talisman gives us strength and courage; it is a reminder of our internal power, particularly when we feel weak and vulnerable.

As another example, albeit with no direct connection with mathematical learning, children wrote autobiographical "I am from" poems and drew self-portraits. A collection of these was compiled and published as a book, *We Are From*, using the self-publishing service of Powell's Bookstore in Portland. The book was showcased at a community meeting, with the self-portraits on display and students reading their poems.

We regard it as essential also to nurture the teachers' senses of cultural, personal, and professional identity as teachers of mathematics. One of the teachers in the project attended her first professional conference in June 2016— by TODOS: Mathematics for ALL—from which she derived great stimulation and enhancement of her sense of self. Other teachers are submitting presentations for conferences on social justice, and we are planning to have academician/teacher teams giving joint presentations.

A general obstacle to our work is that our position on mathematics education as historically, culturally, socially, and politically embedded remains outside the mainstream within mathematics education as an academic field, within typical school practices, within public perception as framed by media, and—arguably to the most extreme degree—with those who hold political power. The field has seen significant changes, notably manifested in the emergence of a group of critical mathematics educators, and NCTM has contributed many publications advancing the cause of treating mathematics as a multicultural subject and teaching mathematics in a way that acknowledges and values cultural diversity (e.g., Hankes and Fast 2002; Secada et al. 1999; Strutchens, Johnson, and Tate 2000). Ethnomathematics as a field of research, a guide for practice, and a political movement has made considerable progress. But the representation of mathematics within the Common Core, as indicated previously, reflects none of this sensibility. Mathematicians often seem to take the position that there is an established body of mathematical knowledge that is culture-free and that the responsibility of teachers of mathematics is simply to transmit a subset of that knowledge, organized in alignment with a logical structure. Most troubling of all: Those who hold political power have superficial understanding of the roles of mathematics in society and the place of mathematics as a school subject. From our perspective, mathematics is granted excessive importance in relation to individual life-paths and societal needs; and as we argued previously, NCTM has contributed to this idea, for example through statements that call "that all students learn mathematics at high levels" (NCTM 2014, p. 4). To repeat the argument made above, expertise in mathematics, and the associated educational and economic opportunities that it affords, should be equitably accessible to all as a civil right (Moses and Cobb 2001); but in recognition of the diversity of roles within society, it should not be demanded of everyone. And we argue that education, including mathematics education, should better prepare children for the most urgent problems facing humanity, which are human, not technical, problems.

Reflecting and Taking Action

As CREME continues, we collectively and continuously reflect on priorities, an effort subject to constraints on teachers' time and energy that are tested by the daily demands of their classrooms, plus demands to align with CCSSM and prepare students for tests. We find it valuable to work within a small core group, but we hope to reach out to more teachers within the schools in the project and to add at least one more school.

We are all too aware of how much more there is to do if we are to have any impact. One of our priorities is to establish sustained connections with the families and communities of the students (Civil 2007), having made a start with the communal celebration of the children's mathematical activities and the event to launch *We Are From*. Such connections require sensitivity to the circumstances of people's lives. And we need to explore how "culturally responsive (mathematics) education" might be characterized for European-American children. "I am from" poems by such children made us aware of the diversity, and hybridity, of cultures indiscriminately covered by the term *European*.

In terms of what happens within the classrooms of the teachers in the project, we plan to pay much more attention to explicit mathematical content, always within the framework of culturally responsive pedagogy. Arithmetic is the first priority. No mathematics educator we know denies the importance of facility with the basic addition and multiplication number facts, and these facts can be learned in ways that, in accordance with one of the mathematical practices highlighted in CCSSM, exploit the structure that is the essence of mathematics, and also acknowledge cultural diversity. In relation to the first, we offer a very simple example:

1. Choose any whole number between 0 and 100 (e.g., 23).

2. Multiply it by 7, and retain only the last two digits (in this case, 61).

3. Repeat step 2 three more times, and see what happens.

(Before proceeding, the reader is encouraged to try this exercise, with his or her own choice of starting number.) This exercise provides practice in multiplication by 7, with the extra benefit of being self-checking: The fourth repetition of the multiplication always returns to the starting number (the reader may like to figure out why), so if it does not, the student can look for the error. In relation to cultural diversity, a simple extension of counting in the home language is to explore alternative algorithms (see the Algorithm Collection Project website, coordinated by Daniel Clark Orey [n.d.] and devices for arithmetic operations, which simultaneously provide opportunities for deepening understanding of arithmetic structures and how the standard algorithms work.

Calculation is only a means to multiple culturally embedded ends, such as measurement and financial transactions, which have rich historical and multicultural manifestations, including those that all children encounter in their contemporary lives in our society. In our view, it is important to understand how arithmetic operations, particularly multiplication and division, are used to model (exactly or approximately) a wide variety of situations. We also plan to work with teachers and students to critique word problems from the point of view of racial and class bias and from the position that they typically present atomistic, minimally contextualized, stereotyped situations, amounting to little more than disguised practice in computation, in stark contrast with the extended Story Line projects described above.

Geometry is another part of mathematics that lends itself to being related to cultural artifacts, such as those available for study in the Portland Art Museum. All cultures produce complex and beautiful designs that afford opportunities for discussing fundamental ideas in two-dimensional geometry, such as tessellations and symmetry, as well as analysis of angles, parallelism, and so on. Moreover, this kind of work allows children to be creative and establishes a link, through a common foundation in pattern, between mathematics and art. Elementary mathematics education could be an intellectual and aesthetic playground rather than the negative experience it is for too many students, remote from their lived experience and doing little to provide them with resources for their future lives.

Currently, we are having badges made for the students that will bear their names and the title "Math Investigator," tangible symbols of a student's identity as an active learner of mathematics. In this way, we are building on activities in which children explore funds of knowledge in their homes and communities in relation to, for example, measurement and designing (see chapter 4 for ways to create these opportunities for students).

On the basis of our collective experiences in and beyond this project, we offer the following suggestions for elementary teachers—indeed, for all teachers. We see these as fundamental questions for which each teacher must construct a personal and deeply considered response.

- Reflect on this fundamental question: What is mathematics education for? Ask yourself, "Am I doing things to my students that are harmful?" If the answer is yes, consider what you, together with your colleagues, can do about it. Seek out activist organizations (e.g., Hagopian [2014], or rethinkingschools.org).

- Examine your own concept of mathematics (Gay 2009) and your own cultural identity. Find out about the ethnomathematical perspective (Mukhopadhyay and Greer [2012] offer a concise introduction) and explore local resources, such as museums, cultural centers, and workplaces that exemplify the mathematical achievements of diverse cultures and groups within contemporary society.

- If appropriate for your classroom or school situation, consider the question posed by Gay (2009): "How can middle-class monolingual European-American math teachers work better with students who are predominantly of color, attend schools in poor urban communities, and are often multilingual?" (p. 189).

- Critique—and ask students to critique—assumptions underlying textbooks and assessment materials. A fundamental problem inherent to textbooks and assessments aimed at mass audiences is this: If they present mathematics in any kind of social context, the situations described will not align with the experience of many or most of the students (see chapter 2 for an example).

- Talk to your students about mathematics, its history, cultural basis, roles in society, and its usefulness to the lives they live and will live. Look for ways to integrate mathematics with other subjects. For example, consider how you might use local resources such as museums.

- Engage with parents and community (Civil 2002, 2007).

- Enroll your students as researchers in their homes and communities to report back on funds of knowledge.

- Most central of all, get to know your students in the richness of their diversity. But doesn't every elementary teacher do that already?

Acknowledgments

The CREME project was supported by grants from Oregon Department of Education, from the Graduate School of Education, Portland State University, and from the Gray Family Foundation, Portland, Oregon.

References

Aguirre, Julia, Karen Mayfield-Ingram, and Danny B. Martin. *The Impact of Identity in K–8 Mathematics: Rethinking Equity-Based Practices.* Reston, Va.: National Council of Teachers of Mathematics, 2013.

Bishop, Alan J. *Mathematical Enculturation: A Cultural Perspective on Mathematics Education.* Dordrecht, The Netherlands: Reidel, 1988.

Civil, Marta. "Culture and Mathematics: A Community Approach." *Journal of Intercultural Studies* 23, no. 2 (2002): 133–48.

———. "Building on Community Knowledge: An Avenue to Equity in Mathematics Education." In *Improving Access to Mathematics: Diversity and Equity in the Classroom*, edited by Na'ilah Suad Nasir and Paul Cobb, pp. 105–17. New York and London: Teachers College Press, 2007.

D'Ambrosio, Ubiratan. "Ethnomathematics and Its Place in the History and Pedagogy of Mathematics." *For the Learning of Mathematics* 5, no. 1 (1985): 41–48.

Esteban-Guitart, Moisès and Luis C. Moll. "Lived Experience, Funds of Identity and Education." *Culture and Psychology* 20, no. 1 (2014): 31–48.

Gay, Geneva. "Preparing Culturally Responsive Mathematics Teachers." In *Culturally Responsive Mathematics Education*, edited by Brian Greer, Swapna Mukhopadhyay, Arthur B. Powell, and Sharon Nelson-Barber, pp. 189–205. New York: Routledge, 2009.

González, Norma, Luis C. Moll, and Cathy Amanti, eds.. *Funds of Knowledge: Theorizing Practices in Households, Communities, and Classrooms.* Mahwah, N.J.: Lawrence Erlbaum, 2005.

Greer, Brian, Swapna Mukhopadhyay, Arthur B. Powell, and Sharon Nelson-Barber, eds. *Culturally Responsive Mathematics Education.* New York: Routledge, 2009.

Hagopian, Jesse. *More Than a Score: The New Uprising against High-Stakes Testing.* Chicago: Haymarket Books, 2014.

Hankes, Judith Elaine, and Gerald R. Fast, eds. *Changing the Faces of Mathematics: Perspectives on Indigenous People of North America.* Reston, Va.: National Council of Teachers of Mathematics, 2002.

Kitchen, Richard S., Julie DePree, Sylvia Celedón-Pattichis, and Jonathan Brinkerhoff. *Mathematics Education at Highly Effective Schools That Serve the Poor: Strategies for Change.* Mahwah, N.J.: Lawrence Erlbaum, 2006.

Koopman, Michael. "Elementary Student T-Shirt Workers Go on Strike." *Rethinking Schools* 32, no. 2 (2017).

Martin, Danny B. "The Collective Black and *Principles to Actions*." *Journal of Urban Mathematics Education* 8, no. 1 (2015): 17–23.

Moses, Robert, and Charles E. Cobb. *Radical Equations.* Boston, Mass.: Beacon Press, 2001.

Mukhopadhyay, Swapna, and Brian Greer. "Ethnomathematics." In *Encyclopedia of Diversity in Education*, edited by James A. Banks, pp. 858–62. Thousand Oaks, Calif.: Sage, 2012.

National Council for Teachers of Mathematics (NCTM). *Principles to Actions: Ensuring Mathematical Success for All.* Reston, Va.: NCTM, 2014.

National Governors Association Center for Best Practices and Council of Chief State School Officers (NGA Center and CCSSO). *Common Core State Standards for Mathematics.* Washington, D.C.: NGA Center and CCSSO, 2010. http://www.corestandards.org.

Noddings, Nel. *Happiness and Education*. New York: Cambridge University Press, 2003.

Oregon Education Investment Board, Oregon Education Association, and Oregon Department of Education. *A New Path for Oregon: System of Assessment to Empower Meaningful Student Learning*. July 2015. http://www.oregoned.org/images/uploads/blog/FINAL_July_2015_Assessment_Document_a.pdf

Orey, Daniel Clark. The Algorithm Collection Project. Website coordinated by Daniel Clark Orey. College of Education, California State University, Sacramento. n.d. http://www.csus.edu/indiv/o/oreyd/acp.htm_files/algprojexpla.html

Powell, Arthur B., and Marilyn Frankenstein, eds. *Ethnomathematics: Challenging Eurocentrism in Mathematics Education*. Albany, N.Y.: SUNY Press, 1997.

Sandoval-Taylor, Patricia. "Home Is Where the Heart Is: Planning a Funds of Knowledge-Based Curriculum Module." In *Funds of Knowledge: Theorizing Practices in Households, Communities, and Classrooms*, edited by Norma González, Luis C. Moll, and Cathy Amanti, pp. 153–65. Mahwah, N.J.: Lawrence Erlbaum, 2005.

Secada, Walter G., Luis Ortiz-Franco, Norma G. Hernandez, and Yolanda De La Cruz, eds. *Changing the Faces of Mathematics: Perspectives on Latinos*. Reston, Va.: National Council of Teachers of Mathematics, 1999.

Sottile, Leah. "The Newest Portlanders: Meet the Refugees from the Most Violent Places on the Planet." *Williamette Week*, September 30, 2015. http://www.wweek.com/news/2015/09/30/the-newest-portlanders/

Strutchens, Marilyn, Martin L. Johnson, and William F. Tate, eds.. *Changing the Faces of Mathematics: Perspectives on African Americans*. Reston, Va.: National Council of Teachers of Mathematics, 2000.

Wiliam, Dylan. *Embedded Formative Assessment*. Bloomington, Ind.: Solution Tree Press, 2011.

Yosso, Tara J. "Whose Culture Has Capital? A Critical Race Theory Discussion of Community Cultural Wealth." *Race, Ethnicity, and Education* 8, no. 1 (2005): 69–91.

Zaslavsky, Claudia. *Africa Counts: Number and Pattern in African Cultures*. Chicago: Lawrence Hill Books, 1973.

ABOUT THE EDITORS

Sandra Crespo is professor of mathematics education in the Department of Teacher Education at Michigan State University. She researches learning and teaching practices that promote collaborative learning and empowerment. She approaches her scholarship in collaboration with colleagues, schools, and teachers committed to social change. Recent publications that embody these commitments include *Smarter Together: Collaboration and Equity in the Elementary Mathematics Classroom* (NCTM 2011) and *Cases for Mathematics Teacher Educators: Facilitating Conversations about Inequities in Mathematics Classrooms* (2016).

Sylvia Celedón-Pattichis is professor of bilingual/mathematics education and a Chester C. Travelstead Endowed Faculty Fellow at the University of New Mexico. Her research focuses on linguistic and cultural influences on the teaching and learning of mathematics, particularly with emergent bilinguals; children's mathematical thinking; and the preparation of teachers to work with culturally and linguistically diverse students. She has worked on several projects with teachers, students, and schools that promote equity in mathematics teaching and learning. Recent publications include *Beyond Good Teaching: Advancing Mathematics Education for ELLs* (NCTM 2012) and "Promising Pedagogical Practices for Emergent Bilinguals in Kindergarten: Towards a Mathematics Discourse Community" (2013).

Marta Civil is professor of mathematics education and the Roy F. Graesser Chair in the Department of Mathematics at the University of Arizona. Her research looks at cultural, social, and language aspects in the teaching and learning of mathematics; connections between in-school and out-of-school mathematics; and parental engagement in mathematics. She has led funded projects working with children, parents, and teachers, with a focus on developing culturally responsive learning environments, particularly with Latina/o communities. Recent publications include "STEM Learning Research through a Funds of Knowledge Lens" (2016); *Common Core State Standards in Mathematics for English Language Learners: Grades K–8* (NCTM 2014); and *Cases for Mathematics Teacher Educators: Facilitating Conversations about Inequities in Mathematics Classrooms* (2016). Civil is also the editor for NCTM's Access and Equity series.